Study Guide for

Design Dimensioning and Tolerancing

by

Bruce A. Wilson

Publisher
The Goodheart-Willcox Company, Inc.
Tinley Park, Illinois

INTRODUCTION

This study guide has been written to supplement the *Design Dimensioning and Tolerancing* textbook. The review questions and application problems contained in this study guide can be completed on the basis of the information provided by the textbook. Other textbooks may be used, but it is unlikely that any other textbook will provide all the information necessary to answer all the questions or work all the application problems.

The textbook and this study guide used together provide the information and practice necessary to gain a strong working knowledge of dimensioning and tolerancing practices.

A majority of the material in the textbook and the study guide only requires an understanding of basic mathematics. Some of the material requires simple algebra operations such as solving for one unknown value when two known values are provided. Knowledge of blueprint reading or basic drafting techniques will be helpful in understanding the illustrations and completing application problems.

To get the maximum benefit from the textbook and study guide materials, the following study methods are recommended.

1. Read the objectives at the beginning of each chapter of the study guide prior to reading the corresponding chapter in the textbook and before a classroom presentation covering the chapter.

2. Read the textbook chapter before attempting to complete review questions or application problems. It is also beneficial to read the textbook chapter prior to a classroom presentation covering the chapter.

3. Complete the review questions and application problems after reading the textbook material.

4. Make a list of questions regarding information that is not understood as you read the textbook materials. Cross off the questions as answers are provided during a classroom presentation. Ask the instructor to provide answers if the presentation does not provide all the answers to your questions.

5. Correct the answers to your review questions and application problems on the basis of classroom reviews. The corrected materials will be useful for studying for exams.

The objectives at the beginning of each chapter in this study guide define what you should be able to do after studying the textbook, completing outside study activities, attending classroom lectures, and completing study guide review questions and application problems. The level of achievement will depend to a great extent on the amount of time devoted to studying the textbook and study guide materials. Full mastery of dimensioning and tolerancing methods requires studying the fundamentals, then applying them to real industrial applications.

Individuals who put forth the effort to become proficient in dimensioning and tolerancing methods and use that ability to maximize drawing clarity and provide maximum permissible tolerances will be rewarded with the satisfaction of knowing that they are producing the best possible results.

Bruce A. Wilson

CONTENTS

		Text	Study Guide
1	Introduction to Dimensioning and Tolerancing	7	5
2	Dimensioning and Tolerancing Symbology	17	9
3	General Dimensioning Requirements	31	15
4	Dimension Application and Limits of Size	63	27
5	Form Tolerances	99	41
6	Datums and Datum References	117	55
7	Orientation Tolerances	143	71
8	Position Tolerancing—Fundamentals	163	83
9	Position Tolerancing—Expanded Principles, Symmetry, and Concentricity	183	97
10	Runout	207	111
11	Profile	219	119
12	Practical Applications and Calculation Methods	233	127

Chapter 1

INTRODUCTION TO DIMENSIONING AND TOLERANCING

READING

Read Chapter 1 of the *Design Dimensioning and Tolerancing* textbook prior to completing the review exercises.

OBJECTIVES

A combination of activities is required to achieve the following objectives. Completing the reading assignment and the following review exercises are an important part of achieving the objectives. Familiarization with the objectives prior to completion of the reading assignment and review exercises will make mastery of the objectives easier. After completing the reading assignment and completing the review exercises, you will be able to:

- Explain the importance of accurately specifying dimensions and tolerances.
- Describe the history and development of dimensioning and tolerancing methods.
- Explain how teamwork can result in better definition of the dimensions and tolerances shown on a drawing or in a computer-aided design (CAD) file, and list job titles of those who should be on the team.
- List the dimensioning and tolerancing skills needed for success in design- or production-related occupations.
- Describe some possible industrial changes and possible impacts of these changes on dimensioning and tolerancing.

————————————————— REVIEW EXERCISES —————————————————

Place your answers in the spaces provided. Show all calculations for problems that require mathematical solutions.

MULTIPLE CHOICE

_____ 1. The wavelength for a specific color of light is used in determining the length of one _____.
   A. foot
   B. yard
   C. meter
   D. kilometer

_____ 2. A(n) _____ is responsible for dimensioning a part in such a way that the functional needs are met and that the part is producible.
   A. designer
   B. inspector
   C. production planner
   D. machinist

_____ 3. Tolerance values should be _____.
   A. assigned to meet the desires of manufacturing
   B. assigned on the basis of what worked on prior designs
   C. selected from a table in ASME Y14.5M
   D. calculated to ensure proper function of the design with consideration given to manufacturing capabilties.

_____ 4. The _____ system is best for accurate measurements.
     A. metric
     B. inch
     C. Neither A nor B.

_____ 5. The preferred metric value for dimensions on a mechanical drawing is
_____.
     A. millimeters
     B. centimeters
     C. meters
     D. kilometers

_____ 6. A machinist might be able to help a designer by telling him or her
_____.
     A. the size tool needed to produce a particular feature
     B. the tolerance that is achievable
     C. about machine capability
     D. All of the above.

_____ 7. One method of reducing the number of unnecessary small tolerances is to
_____ tolerances.
     A. double the value of all assumed
     B. calculate all
     C. remove
     D. None of the above.

_____ 8. Part requirements can be _____ if dimensions are applied in compliance with the standard.
     A. confusing
     B. poorly defined
     C. extremely hard to meet
     D. clearly defined

_____ 9. The application of _____ on a drawing define the amount of acceptable variation on a dimensioned feature.
     A. dimensions
     B. notes
     C. tolerances
     D. None of the above.

TRUE/FALSE

_____ 10. The current standard does not specify a particular measurement unit that must be used. (A)True or (B)False?

_____ 11. The designer should work independent of others to achieve an optimum design. (A)True or (B)False?

_____ 12. The symbol for inches must be applied to all values less than one inch. (A)True or (B)False?

_____ 13. Disagreement about drawing requirements can occur when nonstandard dimensioning methods are used. (A)True or (B)False?

_____ 14. Interpretation of a drawing is the ability to determine part requirements from what is shown on a drawing when the drawing complies with drawing standards. (A)True or (B)False?

FILL IN THE BLANK

_____ 15. The suffix _____ is placed on a dimension when millimeter values are shown on a drawing that is dimensioned predominantly with inch values.

_____ 16. It is necessary to learn _____ system(s) for applying dimensions if a person is to use both the inch and metric units.

_____ 17. A(n) _____ is an ancient unit of measurement based on the distance across a finger.

SHORT ANSWER

18. Why is it important to have an accurate distance standard? _____
_____
_____
_____
_____

19. Give one reason why nonstandard symbols are generally avoided. _____
_____
_____
_____
_____

20. Show a note that should be placed on a drawing that primarily has inch dimensions. _____
_____

21. Why is it important for an inspector to correctly interpret the dimensions on a drawing? _____
_____
_____
_____

22. When is it necessary to know the requirements of a previous issue of the dimensioning standard?
_____
_____
_____

23. How can it be made possible for all paper drawings to be eliminated from a factory? _____
_____
_____
_____
_____

Chapter 2

DIMENSIONING AND TOLERANCING SYMBOLOGY

READING

Read Chapter 2 of the *Design Dimensioning and Tolerancing* textbook prior to completing the review exercises.

OBJECTIVES

A combination of activities is required to achieve the following objectives. Completing the reading assignment and the following review exercises are an important part of achieving the objectives. Familiarization with the objectives prior to completion of the reading assignment and review exercises will make mastery of the objectives easier. After completing the reading assignment and completing the review exercises, you will be able to:

- Identify and draw the general dimensioning symbols and show their general applications.
- Identify and draw the tolerancing symbols and show their general applications.
- Complete a feature control frame using the correct order of segments in the frame.
- Identify basic dimensions and define two means for indicating a basic dimension on a drawing.

———————————————— REVIEW EXERCISES ————————————————

Place your answers in the spaces provided. Accurately complete any required sketches. Show all calculations for problems that require mathematical solutions.

MULTIPLE CHOICE

_____ 1. A value shown _____ is a reference value.
    A. in brackets
    B. underlined
    C. with an arc above it
    D. in parentheses

_____ 2. The origin symbol is _____.
    A. applied to one end of all dimensions
    B. applied to both ends of some dimensions
    C. rarely used
    D. never used

_____ 3. _____ are being replaced by standard symbols.
    A. Abbreviations
    B. Nonstandard symbols
    C. Notes
    D. None of the above.

_____ 4. Symbols on a CAD system are generally _____ to save time when dimensioning.
    A. made part of a library of symbols
    B. drawn to approximate dimensions
    C. omitted
    D. None of the above.

5. Present practice requires the radius symbol be _____ the dimension value.
   A. placed after
   B. placed in front of
   C. larger than the characters in
   D. smaller than the characters in

6. The _____ tolerance symbols are used for specifying requirements that apply to a single feature and doesn't relate the controlled feature to any other feature.
   A. position
   B. orientation
   C. form
   D. runout

7. Feature control frames _____.
   A. have a required format
   B. may be formatted by personal preference
   C. vary between companies
   D. None of the above.

8. Angularity is a type of _____ tolerance.
   A. form
   B. orientation
   C. position
   D. profile

TRUE/FALSE

9. The preferred method to show depth specification is to use an abbreviation for depth. (A)True or (B)False?

10. Ambiguous tolerance specifications can be the result of using nonstandard symbols. (A)True or (B)False?

11. The abbreviation CBORE and the symbol for counterbore may be used on the same drawing. (A)True or (B)False?

12. Datum references in a feature control frame are located between the tolerance symbol and the tolerance value. (A)True or (B)False?

13. A diameter symbol is placed in front of the tolerance value in all feature control frames. (A)True or (B)False?

14. A datum feature symbol may be applied on either side of an extension line without affecting the meaning of the symbol. (A)True or (B)False?

15. Symbols are required to be sized proportional to the drawing sheet size. (A)True or (B)False?

16. Tolerance symbols are generally shaped to give an indication of the required control. (A)True or (B)False?

17. Abbreviations and words rather than symbols are to be used in notes lists. (A)True or (B)False?

18. All feature control frames must show material condition modifiers. (A)True or (B)False?

FILL IN THE BLANK

19. Using symbols _____ the number of words that are placed on a drawing.

_____ 20. There is a quantity of _____ form tolerance symbols.

_____ 21. Feature control frames and datum feature identifiers may be applied to _____ or features of size.

_____ 22. Any tolerance applied to a thread and shown in a feature control frame is assumed to apply to the _____ diameter of the thread unless indicated otherwise.

_____ 23. A _____ may be used to indicate that all dimensions are basic.

_____ 24. A _____ dimension can be indicated by drawing a rectangle around the dimension value.

_____ 25. The abbreviation for regardless of feature size is _____.

SHORT ANSWER

26. The letter X may be used as a symbol. What are the two possible uses of the symbol X? _____

_____

_____

27. Explain how each of the meanings for the symbol X is indicated. _____

_____

_____

_____

_____

28. How is the symbol size determined for a drawing? _____

_____

_____

_____

29. If a drawing is being produced by hand, what is one method of ensuring that symbols are quickly drawn and the correct size? _____

_____

30. List the two types of profile tolerance symbols. The names of the symbols must be given. _____

_____

31. Show the total runout symbol that was used prior to the 1982 standard.

32. What is the order in which datums are referenced? _____

_____

33. List two of the three datum target types. _____

_____

APPLICATION PROBLEMS

All application problems are to be completed using correct dimensioning techniques. Show any required calculations.

34. Show the diameter symbol in the correct location on each of the diameter dimensions.

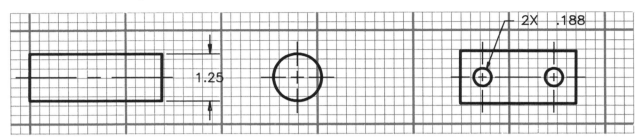

35. Properly show the radius symbol on each of the radius dimensions.

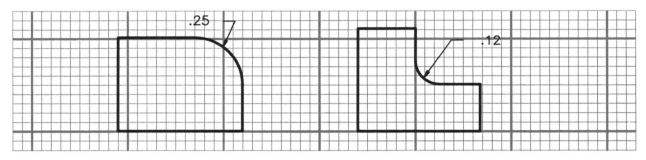

36. Show the spherical diameter symbol on the given dimension.

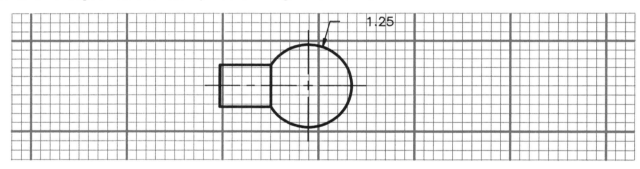

37. Use symbols to complete the hole and counterbore specification.

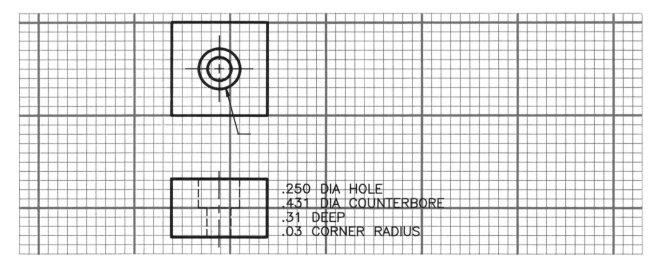

38. Use symbols to complete the hole and countersink specification.

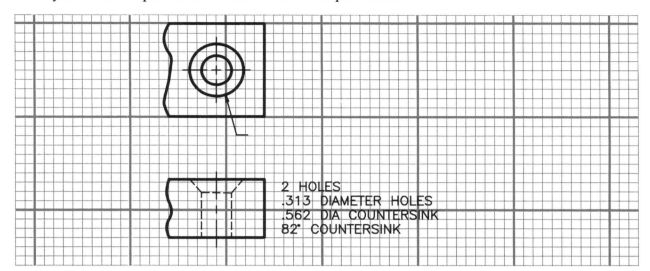

2 HOLES
.313 DIAMETER HOLES
.562 DIA COUNTERSINK
82° COUNTERSINK

39. Label each segment of the feature control frame.

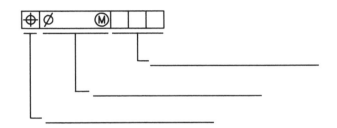

40. Identify each of the given symbols.

⌀   A. _____

⎍   B. _____

∨   C. _____

⌄   D. _____

A   E. _____

⊕   F. _____

—   G. _____

⏥   H. _____

⊥   I. _____

∠   J. _____

//   K. _____

⌒   L. _____

↗   M. _____

⌖↗   N. _____

Ⓜ   O. _____

▲   P. _____

⊖   Q. _____

Chapter 3

GENERAL DIMENSIONING REQUIREMENTS

READING

Read Chapter 3 of the *Design Dimensioning and Tolerancing* textbook prior to completing the review exercises.

OBJECTIVES

A combination of activities is required to achieve the following objectives. Completing the reading assignment and the following review exercises are an important part of achieving the objectives. Familiarization with the objectives prior to completion of the reading assignment and review exercises will make mastery of the objectives easier. After completing the reading assignment and completing the review exercises, you will be able to:

- Apply general dimensioning methods using the correct line types, lettering sizes, and arrowhead form.
- Describe and apply general dimensioning systems including chain, baseline, rectangular coordinate, and polar coordinate dimensions.
- Utilize preferred dimension placement to provide clear part requirements specification.
- Apply general and specific notes on a drawing.
- Cite the general categories of fit between mating parts.

———————————————————— REVIEW EXERCISES ————————————————————

Place your answers in the spaces provided. Show all calculations for problems that require mathematical solutions.

MULTIPLE CHOICE

_____ 1. Extension lines begin approximately _____ inch from the dimensioned feature to provide a visible gap.
   A. .031
   B. .062
   C. .125
   D. .188

_____ 2. Extension lines extend approximately _____ inch past the outermost dimension line.
   A. .031
   B. .062
   C. .125
   D. .188

_____ 3. Extension lines _____ broken where two extension lines cross.
   A. are
   B. are not
   C. may be

4. The recommended minimum distance between adjacent dimensions is _____ inch.
   A. .12
   B. .24
   C. .31
   D. .44

5. _____ dimensions have all values written horizontally.
   A. Aligned
   B. Unidirectional
   C. Metric
   D. Inch

6. A zero is placed in front of values less than 1.00 when using _____.
   A. aligned dimensions
   B. unidirectional dimensions
   C. metric values
   D. inch values

7. Tolerance _____ can be affected by whether chain or baseline dimensions are applied to a part.
   A. interpretation
   B. accumulation
   C. values
   D. None of the above.

8. Tabulated dimensions can be used to specify _____.
   A. location
   B. size
   C. tolerances
   D. All of the above.

9. Dimension lines should terminate on _____ lines.
   A. object
   B. extension
   C. hidden
   D. leader

10. Adjacent dimension values are normally _____ to make them easier to read.
    A. offset
    B. lined up
    C. avoided
    D. None of the above.

11. A(n) _____ view sometimes requires that one end of a dimension apply to a hidden feature.
    A. profile
    B. auxiliary
    C. full section
    D. half section

12. _____ dimensioning is applying dimensions in such a manner as to result in more than one means of defining the dimension and tolerance on a feature.
    A. Double
    B. Duplicate
    C. Ordinate
    D. Third angle

_____ 13. A dimension value placed _____ indicates the value is for reference only.
   A. between quotation marks
   B. inside a rectangle
   C. between parenthesis
   D. between brackets

_____ 14. The difference between the largest shaft and smallest hole is the _____.
   A. clearance
   B. interference
   C. class of fit
   D. allowance

TRUE/FALSE

_____ 15. Size dimensions define the location of features. (A)True or (B)False?

_____ 16. The unidirectional dimensioning system usually requires more space for vertical dimensions than does the aligned dimensioning system. (A)True or (B)False?

_____ 17. Regardless of the drawing scale, dimension values on the drawing must show the size to be produced. (A)True or (B)False?

_____ 18. Visualizing the geometric shapes in a part can help determine what dimensions are needed. (A)True or (B)False?

_____ 19. The view in which a feature is dimensioned may be selected at random. (A)True or (B)False?

_____ 20. Dimensioning between views is not required but can make it easier to relate dimensions to two views. (A)True or (B)False?

_____ 21. Dimensions to hidden features are common since many holes are shown with hidden lines. (A)True or (B)False?

_____ 22. When possible, all dimensions should be placed on a view in which the dimensioned features are seen in true size and shape. (A)True or (B)False?

_____ 23. General notes provide clearly defined information that applies to the drawing. (A)True or (B)False?

_____ 24. Notes must be shown on the drawing sheets that contain the views of the part. (A)True or (B)False?

FILL IN THE BLANK

_____ 25. A leader line has an arrowhead on _____ end.

_____ 26. The recommended minimum distance from an object to the first dimension line is _____.

_____ 27. Notes are connected to features using a _____.

_____ 28. What is the length to width ratio for an arrowhead?

_____ 29. The _____ dimensioning system has values aligned with the dimension lines.

_____ 30. _____ dimensions have coordinate values placed at the ends of extension lines.

_____ 31. Polar dimensions include a distance and _____.

_____ 32. A(n) _____ used to replace one of the arrowheads on a dimension line indicates the origin for the dimension.

_____ 33. A(n) _____ value can be indicated by drawing a rectangle around the number.

_____ 34. A feature control frame contains a tolerance that is _____ to a feature.

SHORT ANSWER

35. When may a leader line be broken? _____
_____

36. List two of the possible arrangements for arrowheads and dimension values in relationship to the extension lines. _____
_____
_____
_____

37. Why are horizontal and vertical leader lines avoided? _____
_____
_____

38. Describe an advantage of unidirectional dimensioning over aligned dimensioning. _____
_____
_____

39. When is it necessary to show the unit of measurement for a dimension? _____
_____
_____

40. Why are larger dimensions typically placed outside smaller dimensions? _____
_____
_____
_____
_____

41. Where may section lines be broken to make dimension application in a section view more clear?
_____
_____

APPLICATION PROBLEMS

All application problems are to be completed using correct dimensioning techniques. Show any required calculations.

42. Show the symbol for each of the following:
   A. Maximum material condition _____
   B. Least material condition _____

43. Circle the dimension value for each of the size dimensions.

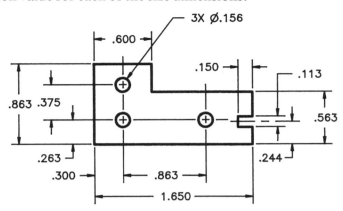

44. In place of each of the question marks, indicate the recommended value for dimensioning.

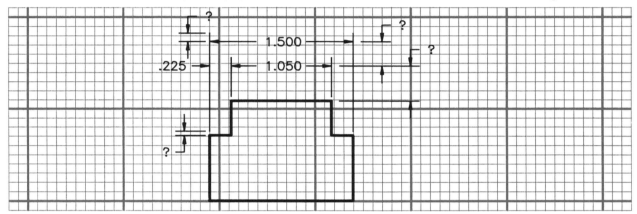

45. Apply dimension values to the shown slot using unidirectional dimensions. The slot is .250″ wide and .125″ deep.

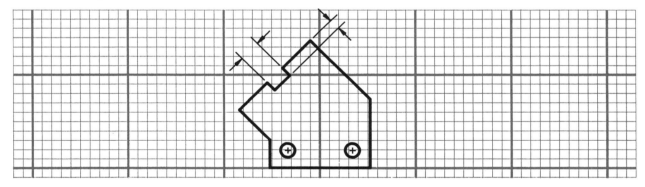

46. A full scale and half scale drawing of the same rectangular part are given. Dimension both of the drawings. Actual size of the rectangle is 2.00″ x 1.00″.

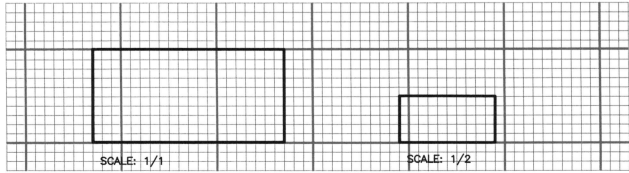

47. What are the maximum and minimum permissible horizontal dimensions between points A and F on a part produced to the given drawing?

_____ Maximum

_____ Minimum

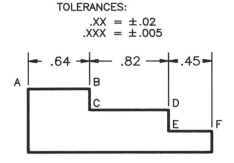

TOLERANCES:
.XX = ±.02
.XXX = ±.005

48. What are the maximum and minimum permissible horizontal dimensions between points C and D on a part produced to the given drawing?

_____ Maximum

_____ Minimum

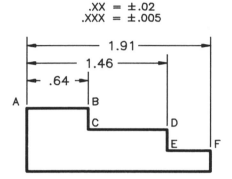

TOLERANCES:
.XX = ±.02
.XXX = ±.005

49. What is the specified size for hole B1 and what is the allowable size variation?

_____ Specified size

_____ Allowable size variation

What is the coordinate location for hole B1?

_____ Coordinate location

What is the specified size for hole A2 and what is the allowable size variation?

_____ Specified size

_____ Allowable size variation

What is the coordinate location for hole A2?

_____ Coordinate location

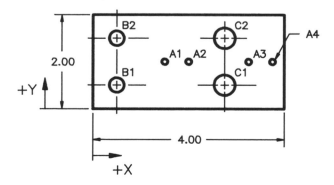

DRILL TABLE

| SYMBOL | LOCATION | | SIZE | TOL |
	+X	+Y		
A1	1.50	1.00		
A2	2.00	1.00	.125	+.005
A3	3.25	1.00		−.000
A4	3.75	1.00		
B1	.50	.50	.312	+.005
B2	1.00	1.50		−.000
C1	2.75	.50	.438	+.006
C2	2.75	1.50		−.000

50. Locate vertex A for the inclined surface and dimension the angle.

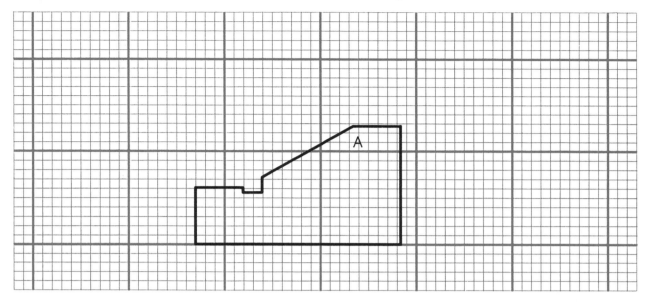

51. Apply dimensions to the given part. Be certain to apply dimensions where the feature profiles are best shown.

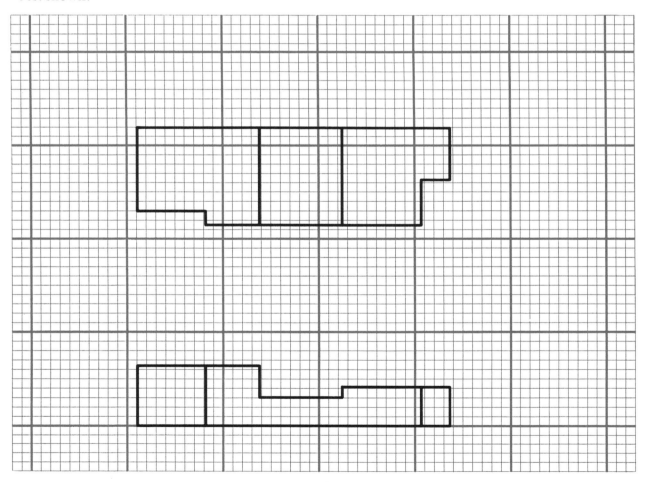

52. Dimension all features.

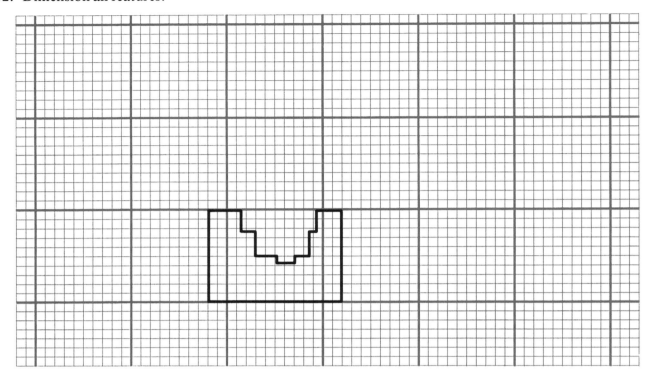

53. Dimension the depth for each slot. Also dimension the location of the hole.

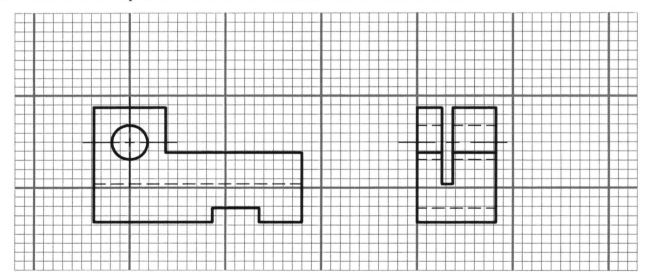

54. Dimension the given part and add section lining (crosshatching).

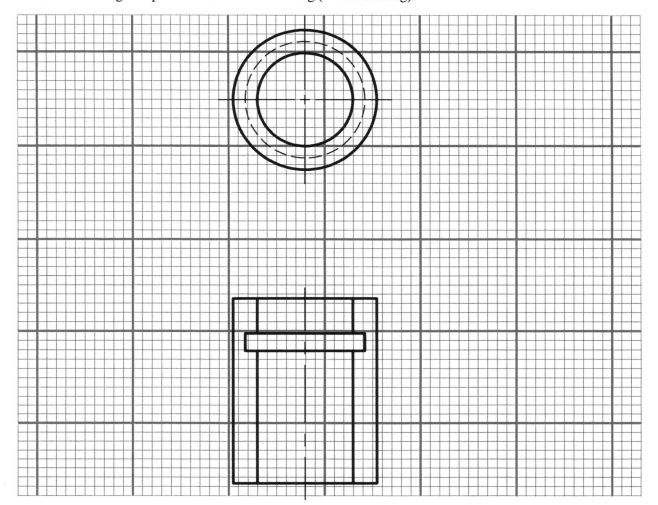

55. Apply 1.0003″ and 1.0000″ limits of size to the outside diameter.

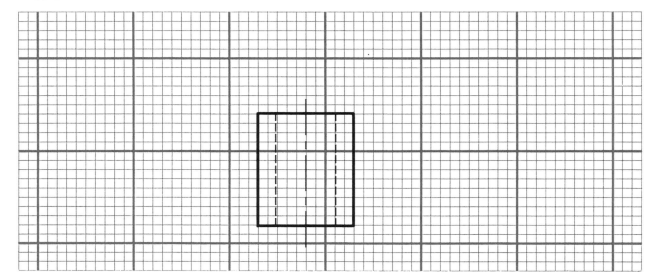

56. Complete orthographic views of the given part and completely dimension the drawing. Select a scale to permit the drawing to fit in the space provided.

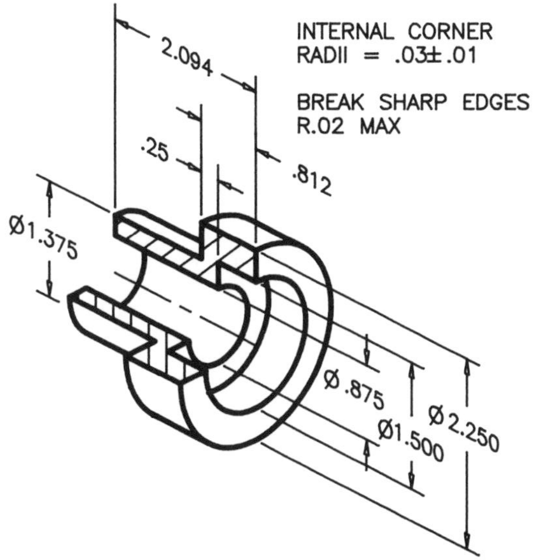

INTERNAL CORNER
RADII = .03±.01

BREAK SHARP EDGES
R.02 MAX

Ø 2.250
Ø 1.500
Ø .875
.812
2.094
.25
Ø 1.375

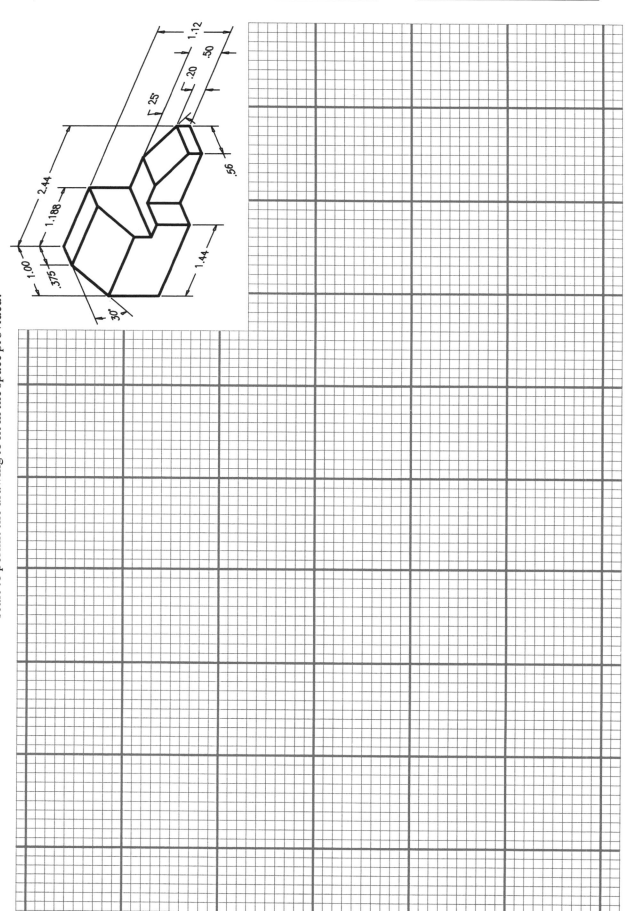

57. Complete orthographic views of the given part and completely dimension the drawing. Select a scale to permit the drawing to fit in the space provided.

58. Complete orthographic views of the given part and completely dimension the drawing. Select a scale to permit the drawing to fit in the space provided.

Name _____ Date _____

Chapter 4

DIMENSION APPLICATION AND LIMITS OF SIZE

READING

Read Chapter 4 of the *Design Dimensioning and Tolerancing* textbook prior to completing the review exercises.

OBJECTIVES

A combination of activities is required to achieve the following objectives. Completing the reading assignment and the following review exercises are an important part of achieving the objectives. Familiarization with the objectives prior to completion of the reading assignment and review exercises will make mastery of the objectives easier. After completing the reading assignment and completing the review exercises, you will be able to:

• Clearly apply dimensions by complying with the stated general dimensioning guidelines.
• Apply dimensions to any of the geometric shapes commonly found on mechanical parts.
• Cite the categories for limits of fit and describe the general condition created by each category.
• Calculate and apply limits of size for mating features.
• Cite the two rules contained within ASME Y14.5M.
• Provide examples of the effects that dimensions and tolerances have on manufacturing.
• Complete a surface condition specification when provided the allowable variations.

––––––––––––––––––––––––––– REVIEW EXERCISES –––––––––––––––––––––––––––

Place your answers in the spaces provided. Show all calculations for problems that require mathematical solutions.

MULTIPLE CHOICE

_____ 1. An angle is assumed to be _____ when lines are drawn perpendicular to one another.
   A. untoleranced
   B. basic
   C. 90°
   D. No assumption permitted.

_____ 2. A right circular cone is dimensioned by giving the base diameter and _____.
   A. cone height
   B. cone angle
   C. Either A or C.
   D. Neither A nor B.

_____ 3. Leaders extending from a hole specification should point toward the _____ of the hole when connected to the circular view of the hole.
   A. center
   B. vertical centerline
   C. horizontal centerline
   D. Either B or C.

4. Hole locations are dimensioned to the _____ of the hole.
   A. edge
   B. bottom
   C. end
   D. center

5. If two groups of holes have sizes that are close to the same diameter, all holes of one diameter may be _____ to make it possible to tell the size of all holes.
   A. labelled
   B. drawn out of scale
   C. omitted
   D. None of the above.

6. It is necessary to specify the diameter, depth, and _____ for a counterbore.
   A. corner radius
   B. diameter tolerance
   C. depth tolerance
   D. All of the above.

7. A common use for a _____ is to provide a recess for a flathead screw.
   A. counterbore
   B. countersink
   C. counterdrill
   D. None of the above.

8. A spotface depth may be specified by _____.
   A. noting the depth
   B. dimensioning the remaining material
   C. Either A or B.
   D. Neither A nor B.

9. Angles are typically dimensioned using values expressed in _____.
   A. degrees
   B. radians
   C. arc lengths
   D. None of the above.

10. The R in a radius dimension is shown as a _____ to the dimension value.
    A. prefix
    B. suffix
    C. Either A or B.
    D. Neither A nor B.

11. Extension lines may be broken where they cross _____.
    A. extension lines
    B. dimension lines
    C. object lines
    D. arrowheads

12. The minimum allowable bend radius for a sheet metal part is affected by the _____.
    A. type of material
    B. hardness condition of the material
    C. material thickness
    D. All of the above.

_____ 13. A bend radius that is too small can result in _____ that weakens the part.
A. ridges
B. sharp corners
C. cracks
D. None of the above.

_____ 14. The maximum limit of size is placed _____ the minimum limit of size when shown in a dimension.
A. below
B. above
C. to the right of
D. to the left of

_____ 15. When using the _____ system, the limits of size for the shaft are calculated to fit the hole.
A. basic tolerancing
B. position tolerancing
C. basic hole
D. basic shaft

_____ 16. A clearance fit used for moving parts is designated by the letters _____.
A. RC
B. LC
C. LT
D. FN

_____ 17. Which of the following classes of fit is most likely to result in a clearance condition?
A. LT1
B. LT6
C. LN2
D. FN4

_____ 18. Which rule in ASME Y14.5M requires perfect form at MMC?
A. Rule #1
B. Rule #2
C. Rule #3
D. Rule #4

_____ 19. _____ include variations known as roughness, waviness, and lay.
A. Limits of size
B. Surface conditions
C. Form tolerances
D. Classes of fit

_____ 20. The standard distance across which roughness is measured is _____ inch.
A. .025
B. .080
C. .250
D. 1.000

TRUE/FALSE

_____ 21. Dimensions to completely define a pyramid are the base dimensions and the apex location dimensions. (A)True or (B)False?

_____ 22. Holes are normally dimensioned by giving the radius. (A)True or (B)False?

_____ 23. A large hole may be dimensioned with the dimension line, arrowheads, and dimension value located within the circle that represents the hole. (A)True or (B)False?

_____ 24. The depth specification for a hole is the distance to the end of the drill point. (A)True or (B)False?

_____ 25. Hole depth should be shown in front of the hole diameter in a hole size specification. (A)True or (B)False?

_____ 26. The dimension line for an angle is drawn as an arc with the center located at the vertex of the angle formed by the extension lines. (A)True or (B)False?

_____ 27. Arcs should be dimensioned in a view where they are foreshortened rather than in a true shape view. (A)True or (B)False?

_____ 28. A centerdrilled hole in the end of a shaft, when used in a machine setup, locates the center of the shaft. (A)True or (B)False?

_____ 29. Every feature of size has a minimum and maximum allowable size, even when a single limit dimension is applied to the feature. (A)True or (B)False?

_____ 30. An RC1 class of fit results in smaller tolerances than an RC4 class of fit. (A)True or (B)False?

_____ 31. Fabrication capabilities and methods do not generally need to be considered when applying dimensions or calculating tolerances. (A)True or (B)False?

_____ 32. The lifecycle costs for mated assemblies can be higher than for interchangeable assemblies. (A)True or (B)False?

FILL IN THE BLANK

_____ 33. The diameter and _____ dimension must be given for a cylindrical part.

_____ 34. A diameter dimension line applied on a circular view is oriented to pass through the _____ of the dimensioned feature.

_____ 35. The abbreviation for counterbore is _____.

_____ 36. A countersink hole specification includes a hole diameter, countersink _____, and countersink angle.

_____ 37. What is the equivalent decimal degree value for 25°30′?

_____ 38. Chamfers made at a(n) _____ angle may be dimensioned with a note.

_____ 39. The leader for a radius dimension extends through the arc _____.

_____ 40. Limit dimensions specify the _____ and _____ acceptable dimension values.

_____ 41. When using the basic _____ system for calculation of tolerances, the basic size is one of the size limits for the shaft.

_____ 42. _____ is the direction of surface lines caused by cutting tools, and may be specified in a surface control specification.

SHORT ANSWER

43. Explain how a single view can be dimensioned to completely define a cylindrical part. _____

_____

_____

_____

_____

44. What is the effect of using very small size tolerances on holes? _____

_____

_____

_____

45. If a pattern of holes is repeated several times on a drawing, why would a removed view be used to define the hole locations within the pattern? _____

_____

_____

_____

_____

_____

46. Define counterbore and list one application of a counterbore. _____

_____

_____

_____

_____

_____

47. How deep must a spotface be made if no depth dimension is shown? _____

_____

_____

48. How is a centerline identified as a line of symmetry? _____

_____

_____

49. What are four pieces of information that must be included in a thread specification? _____

_____

_____

50. How can an exception to Rule #1 be specified? _____

_____

_____

_____

APPLICATION PROBLEMS

All application problems are to be completed using correct dimensioning technique. Show any required calculations.

51. Draw and dimension a single view that completely defines the given part.

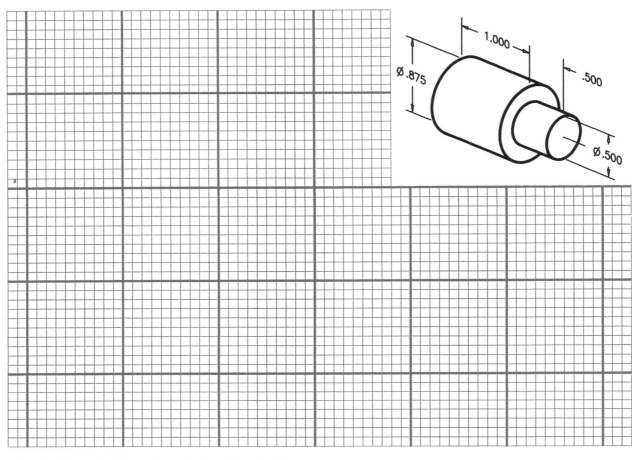

52. Apply diameter dimensions to the given holes.

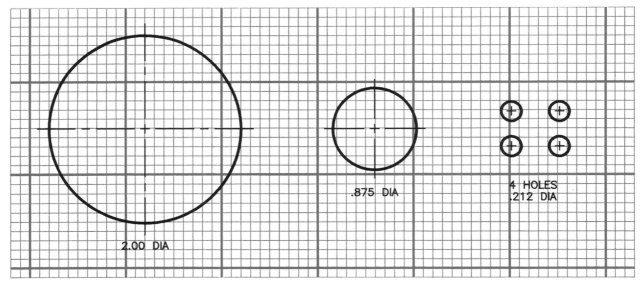

53. Apply a hole specification to the given hole. Use symbology.

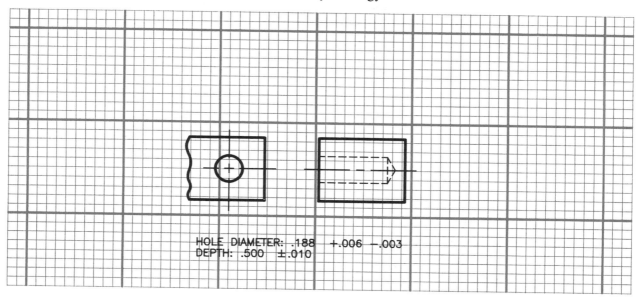

HOLE DIAMETER: .188   +.006 −.003
DEPTH: .500   ±.010

54. Dimension each of the following angles.

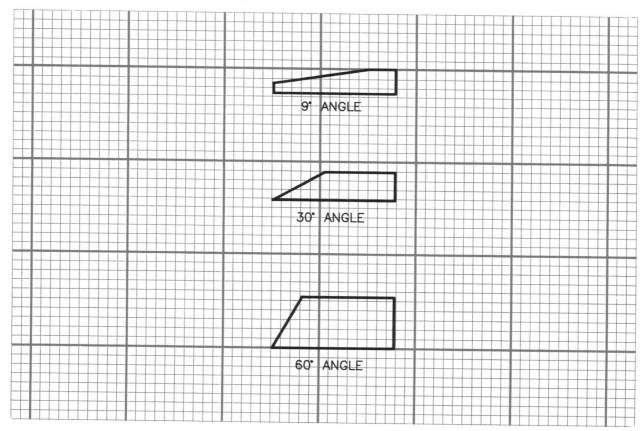

9° ANGLE

30° ANGLE

60° ANGLE

55. Completely dimension each part, estimating dimension values. The arc on one of the parts must be located by dimensioning the tangents. The arc on the other part must be located by dimensioning the arc center. Do not double dimension any feature.

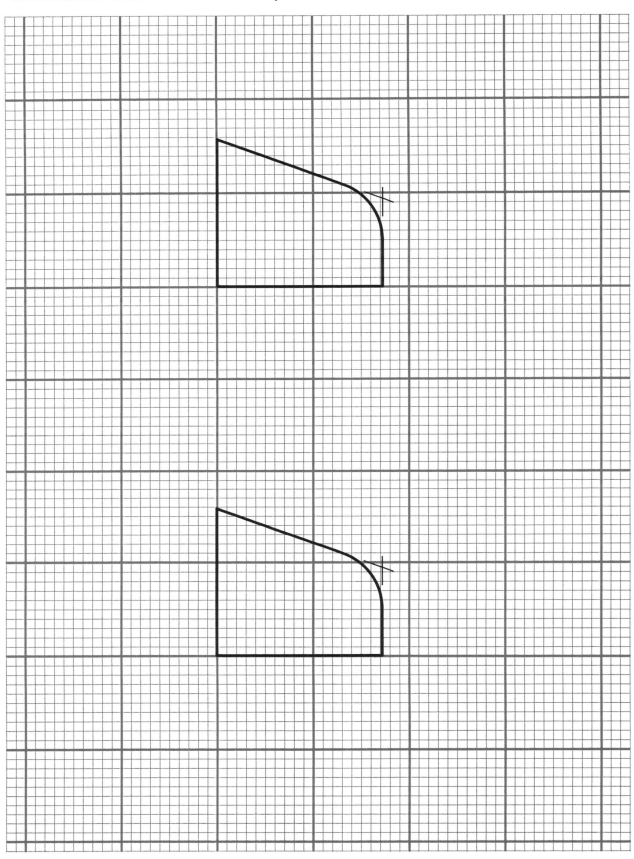

56. Dimension each slot using the dimension values provided.

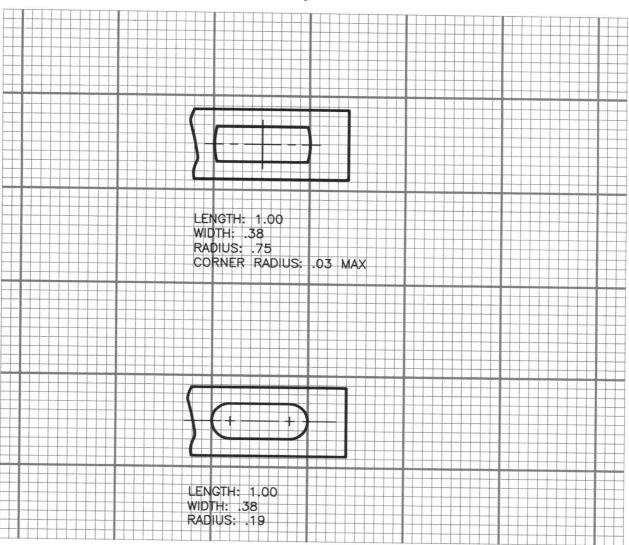

LENGTH: 1.00
WIDTH: .38
RADIUS: .75
CORNER RADIUS: .03 MAX

LENGTH: 1.00
WIDTH: .38
RADIUS: .19

57. Dimension the shaft diameter and the keyseat. Use the dimension information provided.

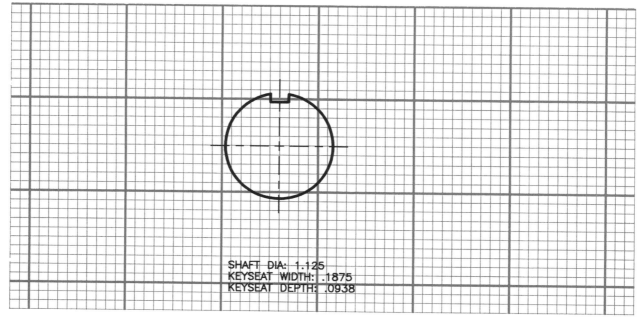

SHAFT DIA: 1.125
KEYSEAT WIDTH: .1875
KEYSEAT DEPTH: .0938

58. Completely dimension the sheet metal part. Estimate dimension values.

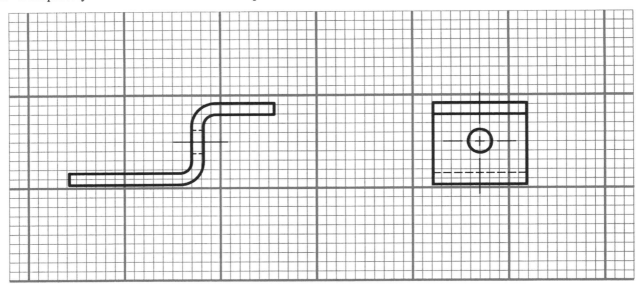

59. Dimension the slot width on each of the given drawings. Use limit dimensions on the indicated part and plus or minus tolerances on the other part. Determine dimension values from the shown information.

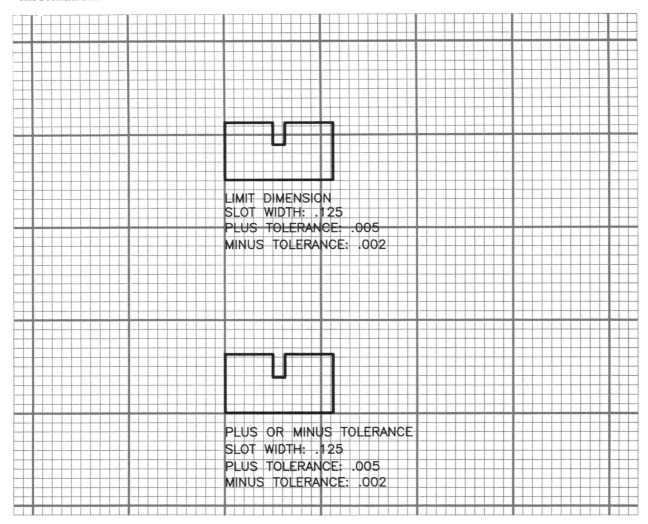

LIMIT DIMENSION
SLOT WIDTH: .125
PLUS TOLERANCE: .005
MINUS TOLERANCE: .002

PLUS OR MINUS TOLERANCE
SLOT WIDTH: .125
PLUS TOLERANCE: .005
MINUS TOLERANCE: .002

60. Add the necessary information to the drawing to permit exception to the requirements of Rule #1.

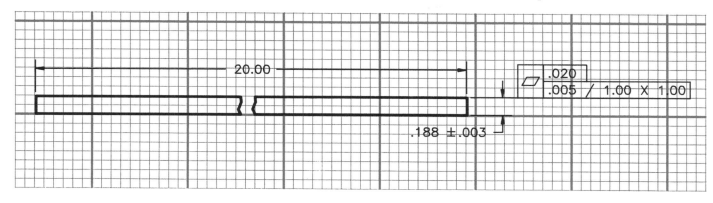

61. Complete the given drawing by entering the information for a revision. The indicated hole was previously dimensioned as a .250″ diameter. It is now to be .261″ diameter with a .006″ plus tolerance and .003″ minus tolerance. Also complete the revision block.

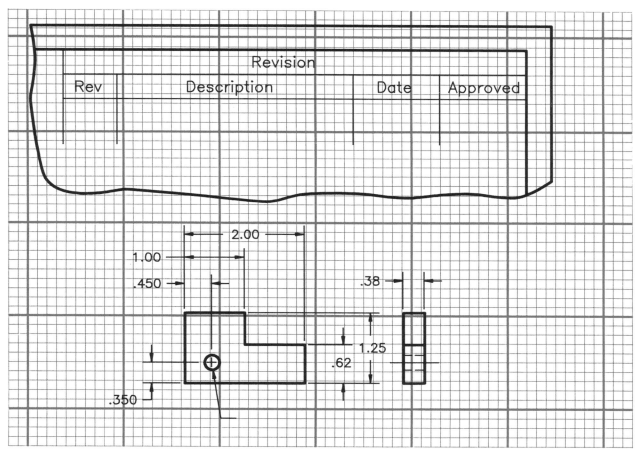

62. Calculate limits of size and apply dimensions for the shown parts. Show all calculations. (See Figure 4-42 of the textbook.) Use tolerance tables in ANSI B4.1 or Machinery's Handbook. Apply the dimensions using limit dimensions.

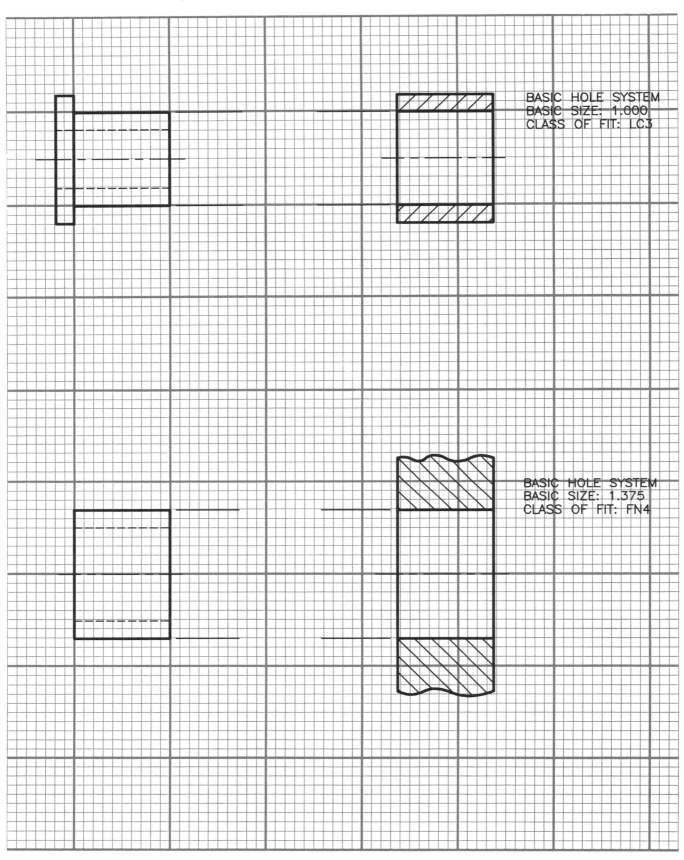

BASIC HOLE SYSTEM
BASIC SIZE: 1.000
CLASS OF FIT: LC3

BASIC HOLE SYSTEM
BASIC SIZE: 1.375
CLASS OF FIT: FN4

63. Calculate limits of size for the shaft and hole. Show all calculations. Split the allowable tolerance evenly between the two parts.

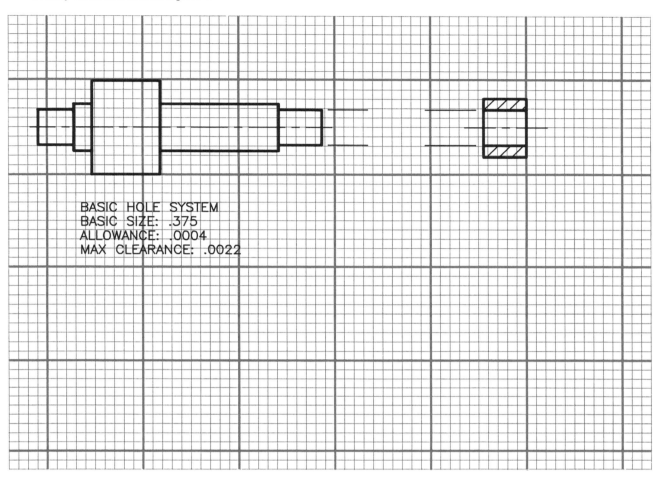

BASIC HOLE SYSTEM
BASIC SIZE: .375
ALLOWANCE: .0004
MAX CLEARANCE: .0022

64. Complete a surface control specification that permits a maximum roughness of 125 and allows a waviness of .001″. No lay direction is required.

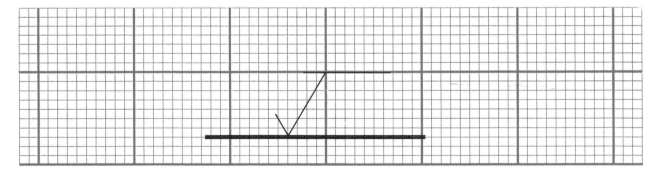

65. Complete a surface control specification that permits a minimum roughness of 63 and a maximum roughness of 250. No additional control is needed.

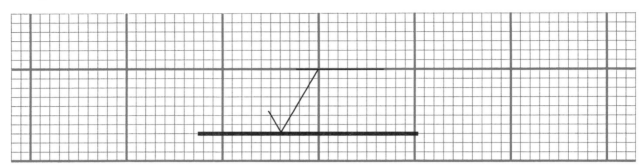

Chapter 5

FORM TOLERANCES

READING

Read Chapter 5 of the *Design Dimensioning and Tolerancing* textbook prior to completing the review exercises.

OBJECTIVES

A combination of activities is required to achieve the following objectives. Completing the reading assignment and the following review exercises are an important part of achieving the objectives. Familiarization with the objectives prior to completion of the reading assignment and review exercises will make mastery of the objectives easier. After completing the reading assignment and completing the review exercises, you will be able to:

- Draw the symbols for form tolerances.
- Complete a feature control frame to specify a form tolerance and properly apply material condition modifiers on the tolerances.
- Explain the extent of form control established by limits of size.
- Apply straightness tolerances to control surface elements or axis straightness and show the interpretation of those tolerances.
- Explain and calculate virtual condition for a hole or shaft that has a form tolerance applied to it.
- Apply flatness to control a surface and show an interpretation of a flatness tolerance zone.
- Apply circularity tolerances and show an interpretation of a circularity tolerance zone.
- Apply a cylindricity tolerance and show an interpretation of the cylindricity tolerance zone.

———————————————— REVIEW EXERCISES ————————————————

Place your answers in the spaces provided. Accurately complete any required sketches. Show all calculations for problems that require mathematical solutions.

MULTIPLE CHOICE

_____ 1. Allowable variations in the shape of an individual feature may be controlled by size and _____ tolerances.
A. position
B. orientation
C. location
D. form

_____ 2. Form variations on a feature of size may not exceed the _____ tolerance.
A. position
B. size
C. orientation
D. None of the above.

_____ 3. _____ feature(s) is/are simultaneously controlled by a form tolerance.
   A. One
   B. Two
   C. Three
   D. Any desired number of

_____ 4. Generally, form tolerances applied on a surface _____ the level of form control established by the size tolerance.
   A. loosen
   B. refine
   C. has no affect on
   D. Either A or B.

_____ 5. Form tolerances are never _____.
   A. larger than the size tolerance
   B. smaller than size tolerances
   C. referenced to datums
   D. without datum references

_____ 6. _____ of ASME Y14.5M defines the assumption regarding material condition modifiers on form tolerances.
   A. Rule #1
   B. Rule #2
   C. Both A and B.
   D. Appendix A

_____ 7. The least material condition for a hole is the _____.
   A. maximum allowable diameter
   B. minimum allowable diameter
   C. actual produced size
   D. None of the above.

_____ 8. Two sides of a rectangular part must be _____ when the part is at MMC.
   A. parallel
   B. flat
   C. straight
   D. All of the above.

_____ 9. Two sides of a rectangular part must be _____ when the part is at LMC.
   A. parallel
   B. flat
   C. straight
   D. None of the above.

_____ 10. Parts subject to _____ are not controlled by Rule #1.
   A. free state variation
   B. damage
   C. mass production
   D. None of the above.

_____ 11. Perfect form at MMC is not a requirement when a straightness tolerance is applied to control _____.
   A. a flat surface
   B. the axis of a cylinder
   C. surface elements on a cylinder
   D. None of the above.

12. A specified axis straightness tolerance on a shaft _____.
    A. also establishes a direct control of surface straightness
    B. has no direct affect on surface straightness
    C. must be specified in a special manner to control surface straightness
    D. None of the above.

13. If exception to Rule #1 is allowed on a feature, then a _____ must be applied on that feature.
    A. small size tolerance
    B. form tolerance
    C. surface finish specification
    D. None of the above.

14. A straightness tolerance used to control axis straightness of a cylinder must include _____.
    A. an MMC modifier
    B. no modifier
    C. a diameter symbol
    D. None of the above.

15. Departure from MMC does not result in any change in the allowable form tolerance if _____ is specified.
    A. MMC
    B. RFS
    C. diameter
    D. All of the above.

16. The virtual condition of a hole is calculated by _____ the MMC size and axis straightness tolerance.
    A. finding the difference between
    B. adding
    C. multiplying
    D. None of the above.

17. Functional gage feature sizes are based on the _____ of the part features to be checked.
    A. LMC
    B. MMC
    C. virtual condition
    D. nominal size

18. The flatness tolerance zone boundary may be at _____ orientation(s) to the part.
    A. only one defined
    B. one of several defined
    C. any
    D. Either A or C.

19. A surface controlled with a flatness tolerance _____.
    A. must also remain within the limits of size
    B. may fall outside the limits of size by a value equal to the flatness tolerance
    C. must be oriented to the referenced datums
    D. None of the above.

20. A circularity tolerance value is the _____ the boundary circles.
    A. radial distance between
    B. diameter difference between
    C. center point offset for
    D. None of the above.

_____ 21. Circularity _____ control surface location relative to the axis of the controlled feature.
A. does
B. does not
C. may

_____ 22. A cylindricity tolerance boundary is composed of two _____.
A. concentric circles
B. concentric cylinders
C. parallel planes
D. parallel lines

TRUE/FALSE

_____ 23. Reducing size tolerance is one method of reducing allowable form variations. (A)True or (B)False?

_____ 24. It is preferable to reduce size tolerance to control form rather than to apply a large size tolerance in combination with a small form tolerance. (A)True or (B)False?

_____ 25. Straightness tolerances applied to cylindrical surfaces have the same effect as when applied to a cylinder diameter. (A)True or (B)False?

_____ 26. A form tolerance applied to a flat surface also controls any surface that is parallel to the toleranced surface. (A)True or (B)False?

_____ 27. Stock materials, such as sheet and plate, must meet the requirements of Rule #1. (A)True or (B)False?

_____ 28. Straightness tolerances are never used to control axis straightness for a shaft. (A)True or (B)False?

_____ 29. A straightness tolerance may be used to control surface elements on a cone. (A)True or (B)False?

_____ 30. An axis straightness tolerance may be larger than the size tolerance. (A)True or (B)False?

_____ 31. Size limits may never be violated regardless of the form tolerance values. (A)True or (B)False?

_____ 32. Functional gages may be used to inspect parts that have tolerances specified with the MMC modifier. (A)True or (B)False?

_____ 33. Unit length control of axis straightness must be specified with a unit length of one inch. (A)True or (B)False?

_____ 34. Flatness tolerances never include datum references. (A)True or (B)False?

_____ 35. A flatness tolerance that is attached to one surface controls that surface plus any other parallel surface. (A)True or (B)False?

_____ 36. Flatness of a center plane may only be controlled by applying a flatness tolerance to each of the two surfaces that establish the center plane. (A)True or (B)False?

_____ 37. Circularity tolerances may be applied to any feature with a circular cross section. (A)True or (B)False?

_____ 38. The four form tolerances are straightness, flatness, circularity, and cylindricity. (A)True or (B)False?

FILL IN THE BLANK

_____ 39. There is a total of _____ form tolerance categories.

_____ 40. All form tolerances are specified in a _____ control frame.

_____ 41. Unless shown otherwise, the material condition modifier on a form tolerance is assumed to be _____.

_____ 42. A hole specification of .375″ ± .005″ diameter results in a perfect form boundary of _____ diameter.

_____ 43. A _____ tolerance specifies how close to perfectly straight a feature must be made.

_____ 44. A straightness tolerance applied to a feature of size is assumed to apply with the _____ modifier unless shown otherwise.

_____ 45. The virtual condition for a .375″ ± .003″ diameter shaft with an axis straightness tolerance of .007″ diameter is _____.

_____ 46. The MMC modifier indicates that the specified tolerance value may _____ as the controlled feature departs from the MMC size.

_____ 47. Additional tolerance gained due to specification of the MMC modifier and departure of a feature from MMC is known as _____ tolerance.

_____ 48. Two parallel _____ bound the tolerance zone for a flatness tolerance.

_____ 49. Two _____ circles bound the tolerance zone for a circularity tolerance.

_____ 50. _____ tolerances simultaneously control circularity and straightness of cylindrical surfaces.

SHORT ANSWER

51. How are form variations on an individual feature controlled to a value less than the size tolerance?

_____

52. List the form tolerance categories. _____

_____

_____

53. A material condition modifier is applicable to the tolerance value when a form tolerance is applied to what type of feature? _____

_____

54. Explain the difference between a surface and a feature of size. _____

_____

_____

_____

55. Define maximum material condition. _____

_____

56. When all features on a part are at MMC, why is it possible for two adjacent features of size to be at an imperfect angle to one another? _____

_____

_____

_____

57. Describe free state variation. _____

_____

_____

_____

_____

58. Describe how an exception to Rule #1 may be specified for a single feature. _____

_____

_____

59. Define virtual condition. _____

_____

_____

60. Explain the difference between a straightness control specified on a flat surface and a flatness control applied to the same surface. _____

_____

_____

_____

APPLICATION PROBLEMS

All application problems are to be completed using correct dimensioning techniques. Show any required calculations.

61. If the bottom surface of a part produced to the given drawing is perfectly flat, what is the maximum possible flatness error on the top surface? _____

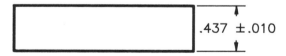

62. Apply a straightness tolerance of .007″ to control the straightness of surface elements on the given shaft.

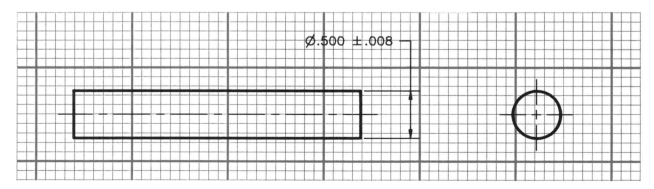

63. Apply a straightness tolerance of .007″ to control axis straightness on the given shaft or explain why it can't be done.

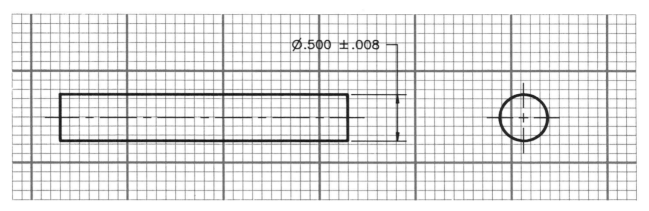

64. Complete the interpretation drawing for the specified tolerances. Add any required tolerance zone boundaries, dimensions, or notes needed to complete the interpretation.

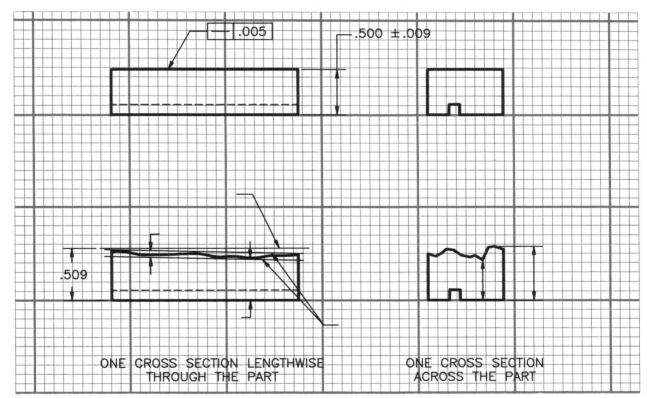

ONE CROSS SECTION LENGTHWISE THROUGH THE PART

ONE CROSS SECTION ACROSS THE PART

65. How many surfaces are on the given part? _____

66. Draw a part illustrating the worst-case scenario in which both features are at MMC.

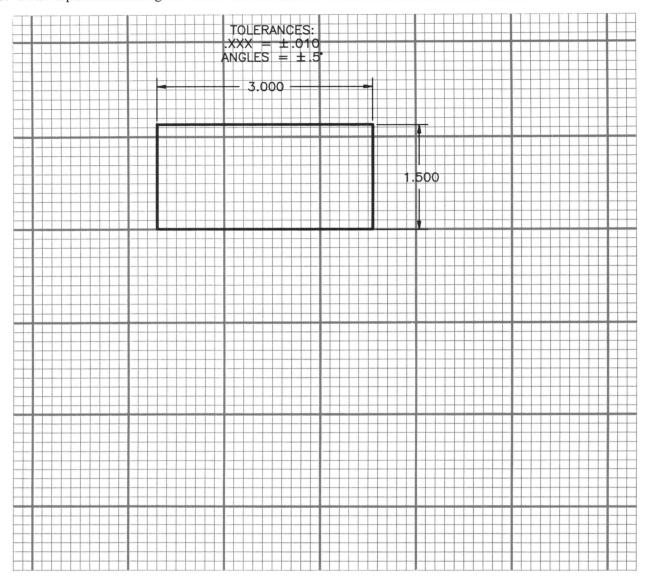

67. Show two methods of applying a straightness tolerance of .008″ on the bottom surface of the given view. Also show a thickness dimension of .750″ ± .015″.

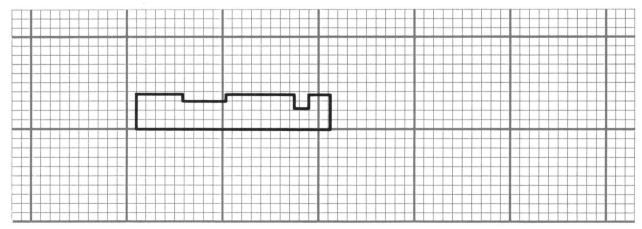

68. Complete a straightness tolerance specification of .008″ diameter to apply at MMC.

69. Complete the interpretation drawing for the specified tolerances. Add any required tolerance zone boundaries, dimensions, or notes needed to complete the interpretation.

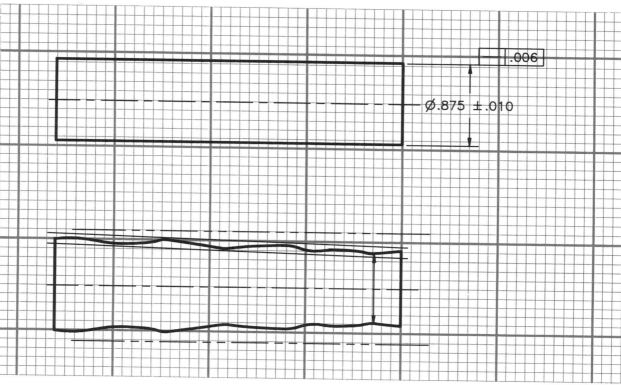

70. Complete the interpretation drawing for the specified tolerances. Add any required tolerance zone boundaries, dimensions, or notes needed to complete the interpretation.

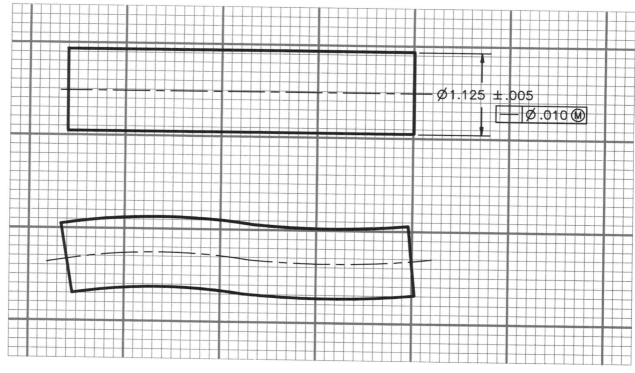

71. What is the virtual condition for the hole? _____

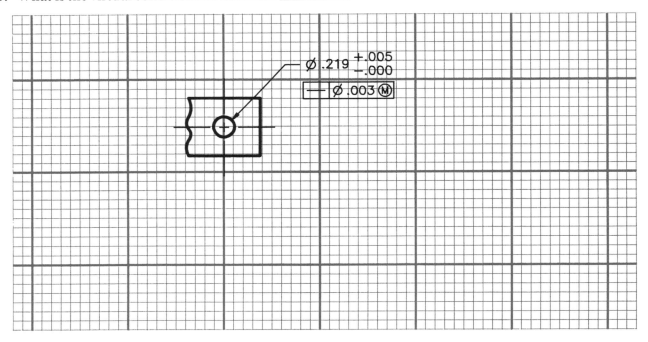

72. Apply a straightness tolerance specification that results in a virtual condition of .216″ diameter.

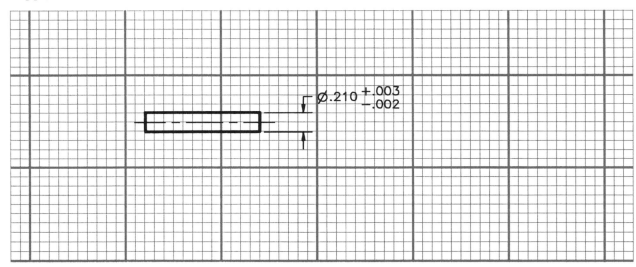

73. Apply a straightness tolerance specification to achieve overall length axis straightness of .015″ diameter at MMC and unit length axis straightness of .005″ diameter per 1.00″ of length.

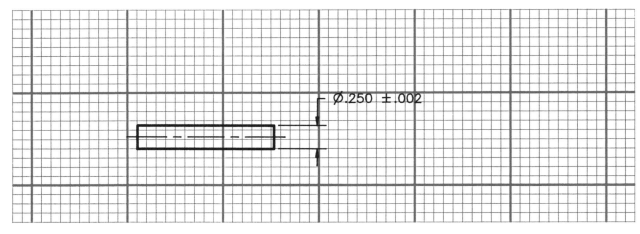

74. Sketch a gage to check the unit length specification in the given figure. Apply dimensions to show the theoretical dimensions for a perfect gage. Do not apply gage tolerances.

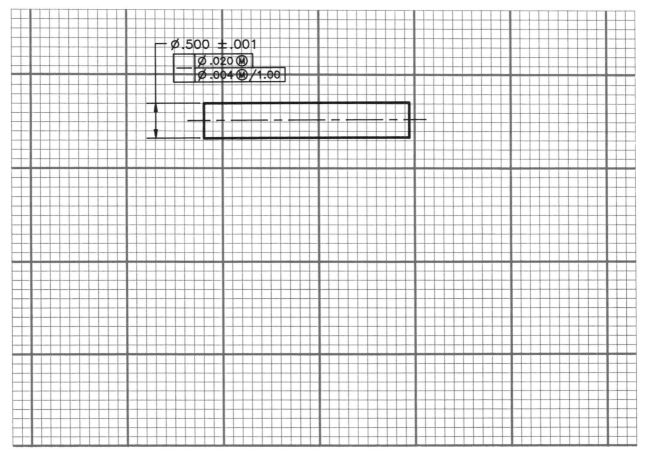

75. Show two methods of applying a flatness tolerance of .010″ on one of the large surfaces on the part in the following illustration.

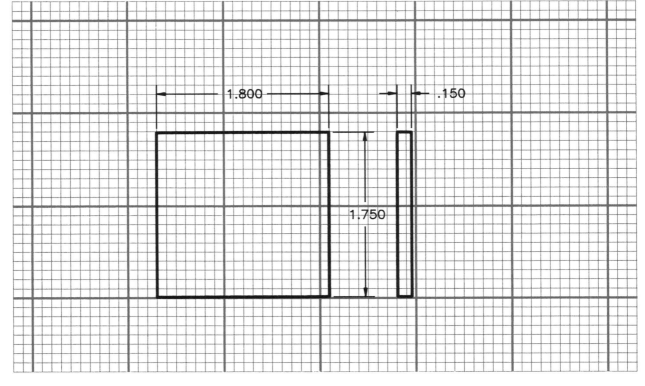

76. Complete the interpretation drawing for the specified tolerances. Add any required tolerance zone boundaries, dimensions, or notes needed to complete the interpretation.

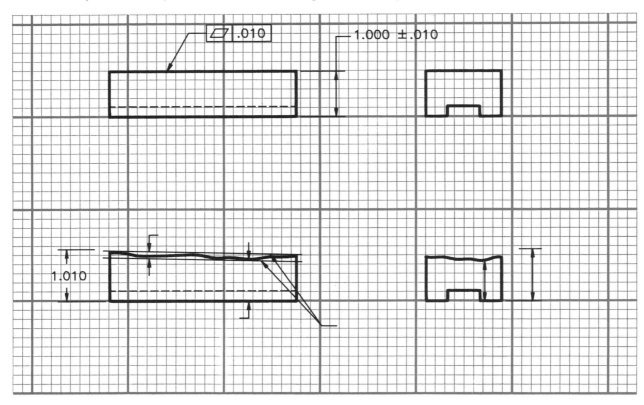

77. Draw a feature control frame that establishes an overall flatness tolerance of .020″ and a unit area flatness of .009″ per square inch.

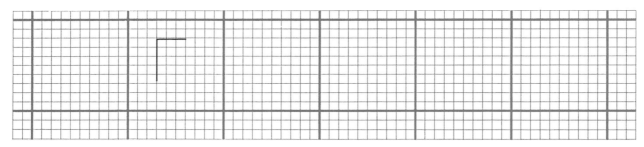

78. Apply a circularity tolerance that permits one-half the amount of form variation that would be permitted by the given size tolerance.

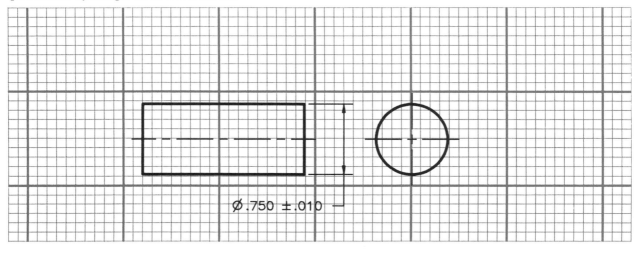

79. Complete the interpretation drawing for the specified tolerances. Add any required tolerance zone boundaries, dimensions, or notes needed to complete the interpretation.

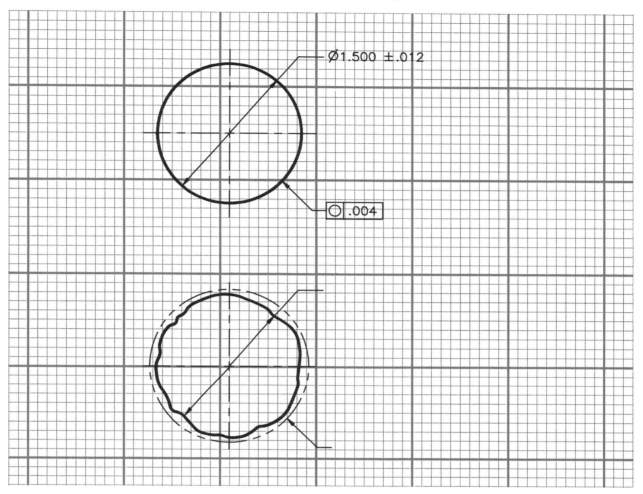

80. Apply a tolerance specification that requires surface conditions to fall within two concentric cylinders separated by .005″.

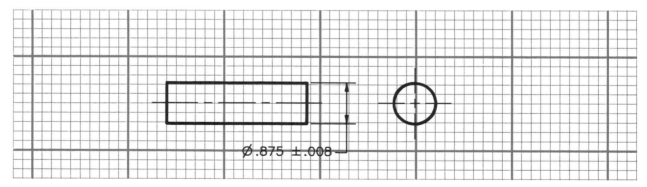

81. A shaft is produced at a diameter of .559″. The specified size is .562″ ± .004″ and an axis straightness tolerance of .003″ diameter at MMC is specified. What is the allowable straightness error on the produced part? _____

Chapter 6

DATUMS AND DATUM REFERENCES

READING

Read Chapter 6 of the *Design Dimensioning and Tolerancing* textbook prior to completing the review exercises.

OBJECTIVES

A combination of activities is required to achieve the following objectives. Completing the reading assignment and the following review exercises are an important part of achieving the objectives. Familiarization with the objectives prior to completion of the reading assignment and review exercises will make mastery of the objectives easier. After completing the reading assignment and completing the review exercises, you will be able to:

- Define the difference between a theoretically perfect datum and a datum feature.
- Explain how to create a datum reference frame through references made on a drawing.
- Utilize all methods for identifying datum features, including the use of target points, lines, and areas.
- Make datum references in a feature control frame using the correct order of precedence.
- Explain how a datum reference frame is established from three referenced datum surfaces.
- Use material condition modifiers on datum references and be able to explain the significance of the modifiers.

————————————————————— REVIEW EXERCISES —————————————————————

Place your answers in the spaces provided. Accurately complete any required sketches. Show all calculations for problems that require mathematical solutions.

MULTIPLE CHOICE

_____ 1. Datum references may be contained in a _____.
A. datum reference frame
B. feature control frame
C. datum system
D. machine part

_____ 2. A tolerance specification shown in a feature control frame may include _____ datum reference(s).
A. one
B. two
C. three
D. All of the above.

_____ 3. The first datum reference in a tolerance specification identifies the _____ datum reference.
A. primary
B. secondary
C. tertiary
D. None of the above.

_____ 4. Planes in a datum reference frame are always _____.
   A. perfect
   B. mutually perpendicular
   C. Both A and B.
   D. Neither A nor B.

_____ 5. The factor that is least important when selecting datum references for a tolerance specification is _____.
   A. functional requirements
   B. fabrication methods
   C. inspection methods
   D. alphabetical order of datum letters

_____ 6. The datum target symbol is used to identify datum _____.
   A. targets
   B. features
   C. planes
   D. axes

_____ 7. A datum target symbol is a circle with a _____ line across it.
   A. vertical
   B. horizontal
   C. diagonal
   D. Both A and B.

_____ 8. A surface plate or other tooling device used to contact a datum feature acts as a datum _____.
   A. plane
   B. simulator
   C. axis
   D. reference frame

_____ 9. A primary reference to a cylindrical datum feature establishes a _____.
   A. datum axis
   B. datum plane
   C. coordinate system
   D. centerline

_____ 10. A _____ leader extending from a datum target symbol to a datum target indicates the target is on the far side of the object.
   A. solid
   B. dashed
   C. phantom
   D. None of the above.

_____ 11. Single point contact at a target point can be achieved with a _____ tooling post.
   A. flat-ended
   B. hollow point
   C. spherical-ended
   D. None of the above.

_____ 12. An end view of a _____ is shown with the same symbol as a target point.
   A. target line
   B. target area
   C. datum surface
   D. None of the above.

_____ 13. Target areas have a _____ shape.
A. round
B. square
C. rectangular
D. Any of the above.

_____ 14. _____ datum reference frame(s) is/are created if one feature control frame references datum A primary, B secondary, and C tertiary; and another feature control frame references datum B primary, C secondary, and A tertiary.
A. one
B. two
C. three
D. Any of the above.

_____ 15. A flat surface on a part will stabilize on _____ point(s) or more when set on a surface plate.
A. one
B. two
C. three
D. None of the above.

_____ 16. Datum _____ is a means of approximating the theoretical location of the datums.
A. referencing
B. identification
C. targeting
D. simulation

_____ 17. Identifying a hole as a datum feature is a means of establishing a _____.
A. datum axis
B. datum plane
C. datum target
D. virtual condition

_____ 18. A datum feature symbol placed _____ identifies a datum feature of size.
A. on an extension line
B. anywhere
C. on an object line
D. on a dimension line

_____ 19. A reference to datum A primary, B secondary, and C tertiary creates _____ a reference to datum A primary, C secondary, and B tertiary.
A. the same datum reference frame as
B. the same coordinate system as
C. a different datum reference frame than
D. None of the above.

_____ 20. Multiple groups of features are assumed to _____ if the tolerance specifications on the groups reference the same datums in the same order of precedence.
A. create one pattern
B. create multiple patterns
C. create confusion
D. Both B and C.

_____ 21. There must be at least _____ target point(s) identified for a flat surface that is referenced as a primary datum.
A. one
B. two
C. three
D. four

_____ 22. The distance between stepped datum targets is defined with _____.
A. basic dimensions
B. limit dimensions
C. plus or minus tolerances
D. None of the above.

_____ 23. _____ targets are used to establish a datum plane by contacting features in a manner that causes the feature to center.
A. Equalizing
B. Small
C. Large
D. Stepped

TRUE/FALSE

_____ 24. Datum features are typically identified by attaching symbols to centerlines and other theoretical entities. (A)True or (B)False?

_____ 25. Tolerance specifications that reference datums require that measurements be verified relative to the datums rather than to the imperfect part surfaces. (A)True or (B)False?

_____ 26. The letter used for a primary datum reference must precede the letter in the alphabet used for a secondary datum reference. (A)True or (B)False?

_____ 27. Using implied datums is permitted since this practice saves time. (A)True or (B)False?

_____ 28. A datum target point shown on a drawing indicates that the target location is to make point contact with the tooling. (A)True or (B)False?

_____ 29. Contact with a datum target line on a flat surface may be achieved by contacting the side of a dowel pin. (A)True or (B)False?

_____ 30. The perimeter of a target area must always be shown with a phantom line. (A)True or (B)False?

_____ 31. Datum precedence shown in a feature control frame affects how the datum features are used to establish a datum reference frame. (A)True or (B)False?

_____ 32. A secondary datum feature that is produced with an angular error relative to the primary datum feature causes the datum reference frame to be distorted. (A)True or (B)False?

_____ 33. The minimum number of points on a flat surface that must make contact to establish a secondary datum plane is two. (A)True or (B)False?

_____ 34. A datum feature triangle should not be attached to a dimension line. (A)True or (B)False?

_____ 35. Before a means of datum simulation can be determined, it is necessary to know the order of precedence of all datums and the material condition modifier for each reference to a datum feature of size. (A)True or (B)False?

_____ 36. A datum feature can't be referenced as a primary datum in one specification and as a secondary datum in another specification. (A)True or (B)False?

_____ 37. Compound datum features are two features used to establish one datum. (A)True or (B)False?

_____ 38. ASME Y14.5M specifies that datum feature symbols should not be shown on centerlines. (A)True or (B)False?

_____ 39. Datum targets are permitted on cylindrical features such as holes and shafts. (A)True or (B)False?

_____ 40. More than three datum targets may be placed on a single datum feature. (A)True or (B)False?

_____ 41. It is a poor practice to combine datum target areas and datum target points on the same datum feature. (A)True or (B)False?

FILL IN THE BLANK

_____ 42. A datum reference frame made up of three mutually perpendicular planes may be established by referencing _____ datum(s) that are located by surfaces.

_____ 43. _____ are used to identify surfaces and features of size as datum features.

_____ 44. A datum _____ is established by a flat surface that is identified as a datum feature.

_____ 45. A _____ line (type) is normally used to show the perimeter of a datum target area.

_____ 46. A primary datum feature establishes location of the first plane in the _____.

_____ 47. _____ points are required to define a plane.

_____ 48. The secondary datum plane in a datum reference frame must be oriented _____ to the primary plane.

_____ 49. _____ flat surfaces must be referenced to establish three planes in a datum reference frame.

_____ 50. The diameter of a round target area may be shown in the _____ half of the datum target symbol.

_____ 51. The order of datum _____ shown in a feature control frame must be considered when defining datum targets on a drawing.

_____ 52. If a primary datum plane is established by a flat surface, _____ holes must be referenced as datum features to completely establish and clock the datum reference frame?

_____ 53. Features that lie in more than one plane are called _____ features when they are used to establish one datum plane.

_____ 54. If a primary datum reference is to a datum feature of size and the reference includes the MMC modifier, then the datum simulator size is equal to the _____ of the datum feature.

_____ 55. If a secondary datum reference is to a datum feature of size and the reference includes the MMC modifier, then the datum simulator size is equal to the _____ of the datum feature.

SHORT ANSWER

56. What is the difference between a datum feature and a datum? _____
_____
_____
_____

57. List two types of tolerance specifications that require datum references. _____
_____
_____

58. State one reason why it is preferable to measure from a datum reference frame rather than from datum features. _____
_____
_____
_____

59. Explain why it is ambiguous to place a datum feature symbol on the centerline of a counterbored hole. _____
_____
_____
_____

60. Describe two methods for applying a datum feature symbol to indicate that a flat surface is a datum feature. _____
_____
_____
_____

61. List the three types of datum targets. _____
_____
_____

62. Explain why at least three target points are needed on a surface that is referenced as a primary datum. _____
_____
_____
_____

63. List one factor that should be considered when determining the size of a datum target area, and explain why the factor should be considered. _____
_____
_____
_____

64. If a workpiece is considered unstable on the primary datum simulator, what may be done?

_____

_____

65. What is the result of applying a datum feature symbol to the width dimension on a slot?

_____

_____

66. When are material condition modifiers applicable on datum references? _____

_____

_____

67. What is the difference between datum reference A-B and AB? _____

_____

_____

_____

_____

APPLICATION PROBLEMS

All application problems are to be completed using correct dimensioning techniques. Show any required calculations.

68. Identify the order of precedence for each of the datum letters.

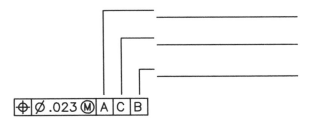

69. Identify a datum reference, a datum feature, and a datum plane.

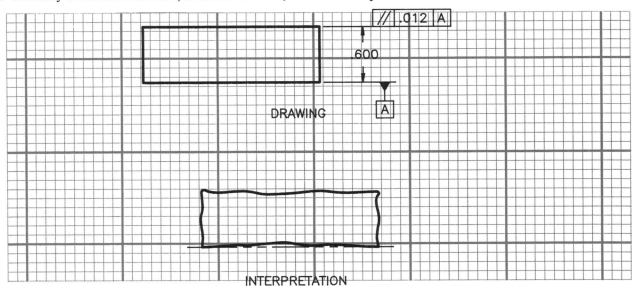

70. Sketch a datum reference frame for the given part. Assume that a tolerance specification references datum A primary, B secondary, and C tertiary. Label each of the datum planes on the datum reference frame. Show the part in the datum reference frame.

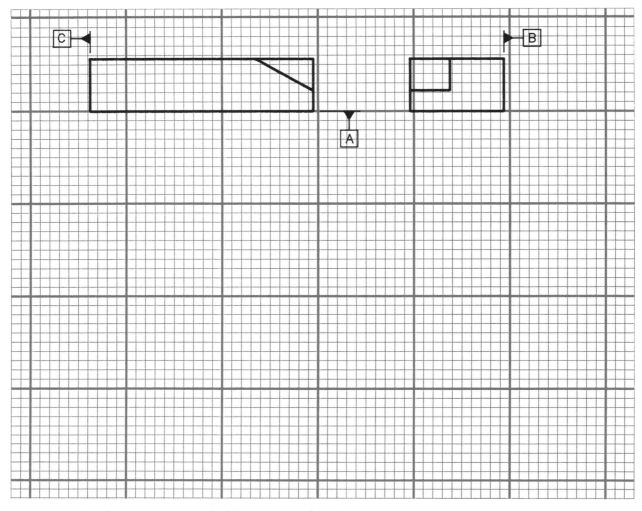

71. Complete the datum target symbol for target point A3.

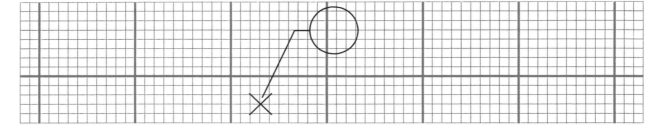

72. Identify the diameter of the given cylinder as datum feature A so that a datum axis is established.

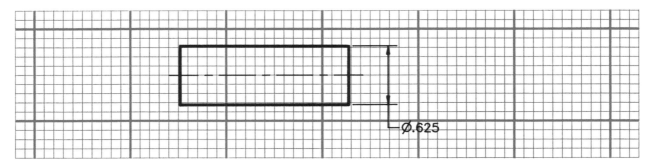

Ø.625

73. Show, label, and locate datum targets on the given part. Use target types appropriate for a small casting, and use a number of targets that permits datum references in the order of precedence shown in the given drawing.

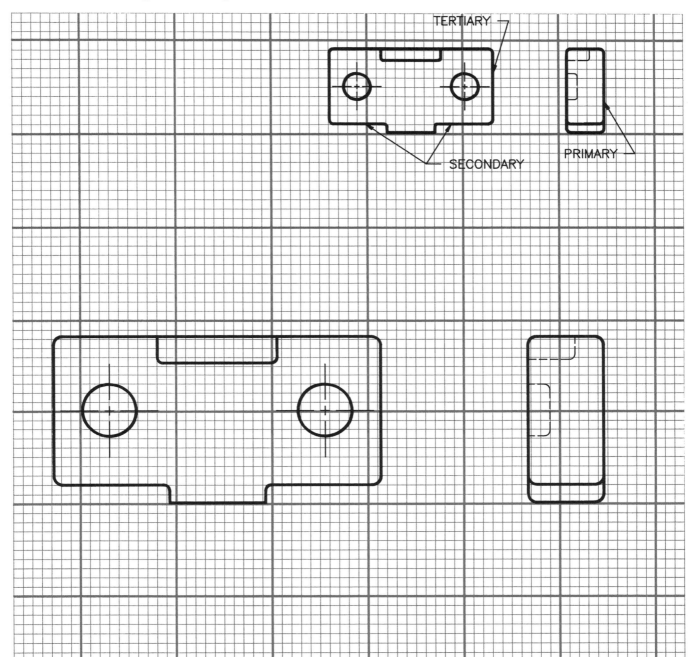

74. Identify each of the given symbols.

×   A. _____

_ _ _ _   B. _____

  C. _____

75. Complete the given feature control frame. Reference datum D primary, B secondary, and C tertiary.

$$\boxed{\oplus} \ \boxed{\varnothing\ .015\ \text{\small{M}}} \ \boxed{}\ \boxed{}\ \boxed{}$$

76. Identify the shaft diameter as datum feature A and the right end as datum feature B.

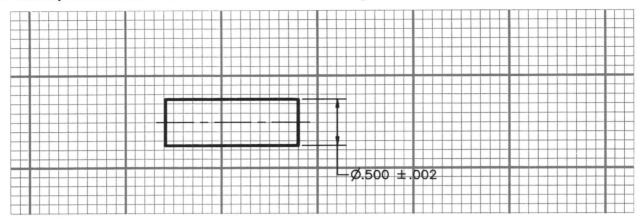

Ø.500 ±.002

77. Sketch a tool that properly locates the datum reference frame for the given part. Show possible points of contact with the part.

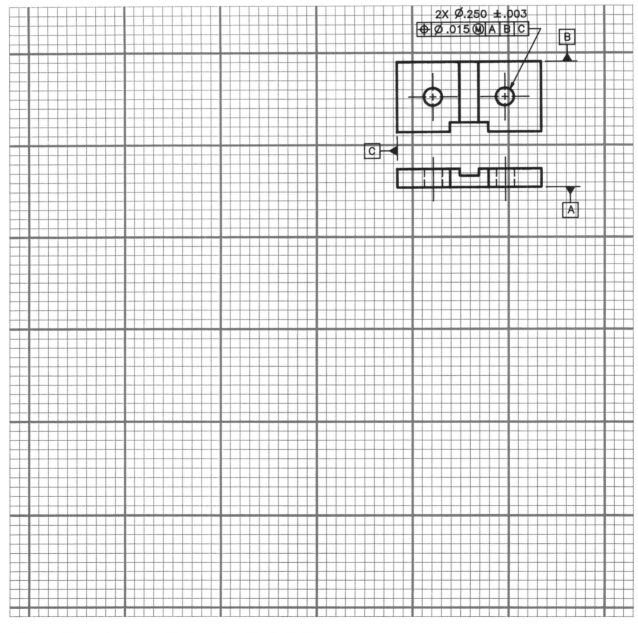

2X Ø.250 ±.003

⊕ Ø.015 Ⓜ A B C

78. Sketch and dimension the gage features required to establish the datum reference frame for the shown part. Superimpose the gage on the given views.

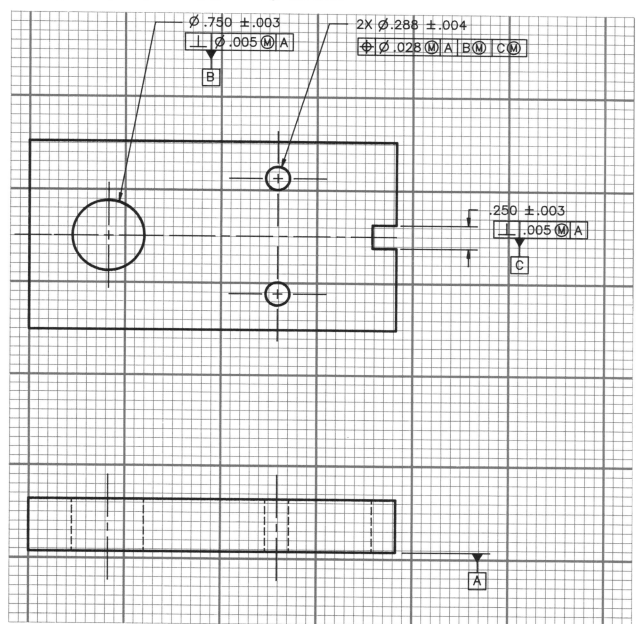

79. The bottom surface of the shown part is referenced in two feature control frames. It is referenced as primary datum A in one specification. It is referenced as secondary datum E in another specification. Specify targets that permit the two datum references.

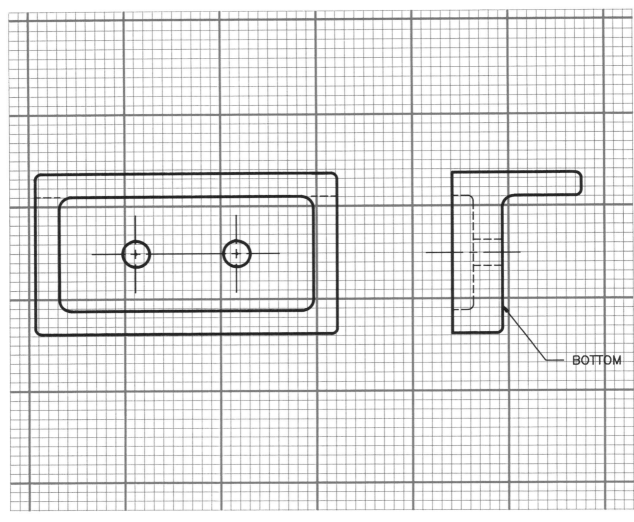

80. Identify the centerdrill countersinks as datum features A and B. Complete the total runout specification by showing a datum reference to compound datums A and B.

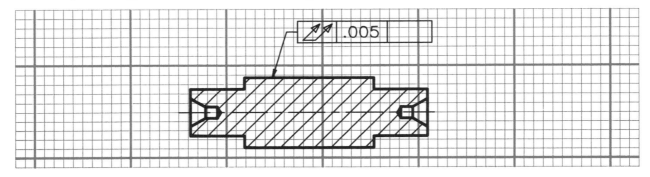

81. Explain why the shown drawing is wrong and correct the drawing. _____
_____
_____
_____

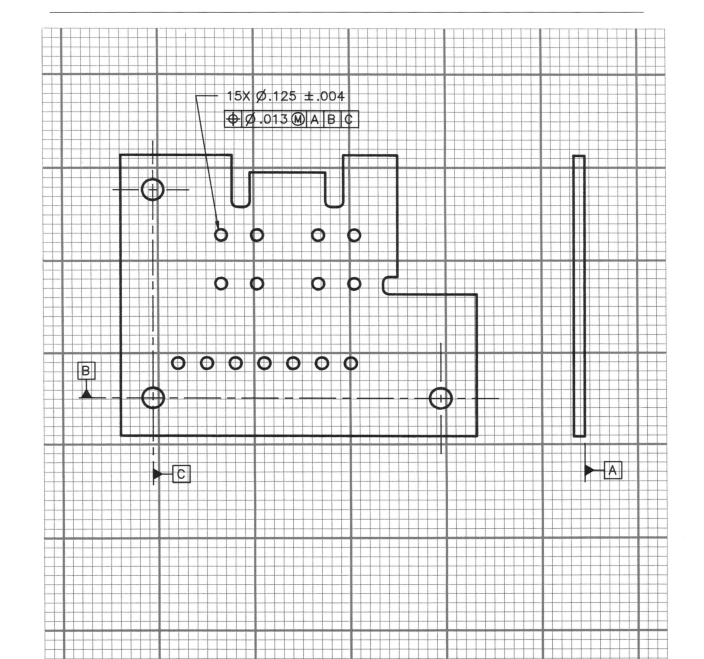

82. Sketch the datum simulators required for the given part. Apply nominal size and location dimensions for the simulators.

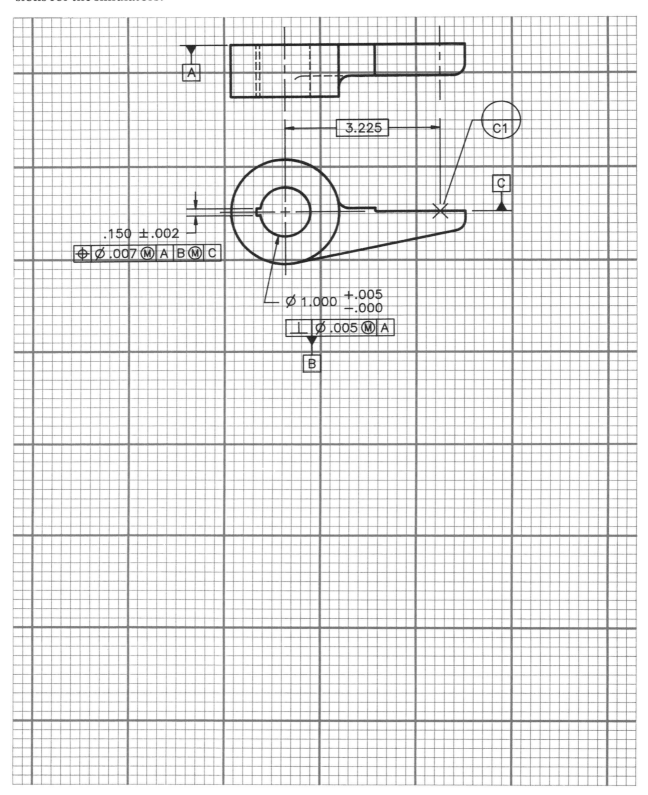

83. A front and bottom view of the part are shown to permit proper application of dimensions. Sketch the datum simulators required for the given part. Apply nominal location dimensions for the target point locators. A front and top view of the datum simulators will be needed.

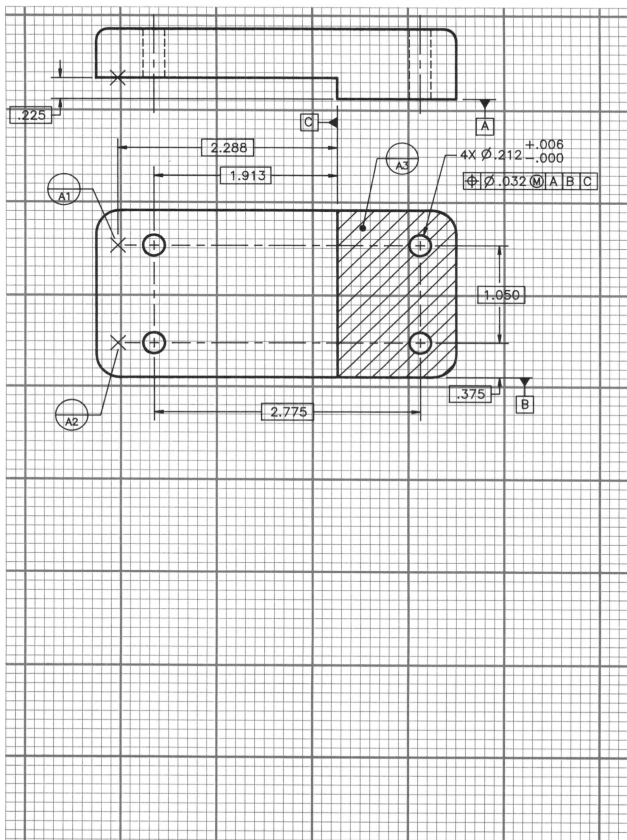

84. Complete the interpretation drawing. Include datums and the dimensions to the tolerance zone for the one dimensioned feature that is related to the datum reference frame.

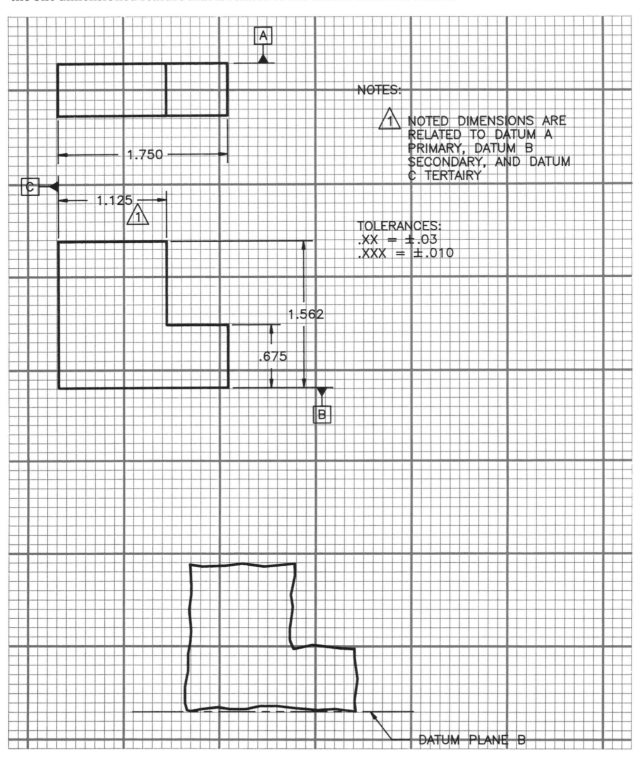

NOTES:

⚠1 NOTED DIMENSIONS ARE RELATED TO DATUM A PRIMARY, DATUM B SECONDARY, AND DATUM C TERTAIRY

TOLERANCES:
.XX = ±.03
.XXX = ±.010

1.750

C

1.125
⚠1

1.562

.675

A

B

DATUM PLANE B

Chapter 7

ORIENTATION TOLERANCES

READING

Read Chapter 7 of the *Design Dimensioning and Tolerancing* textbook prior to completing the review exercises.

OBJECTIVES

A combination of activities is required to achieve the following objectives. Completing the reading assignment and the following review exercises are an important part of achieving the objectives. Familiarization with the objectives prior to completion of the reading assignment and review exercises will make mastery of the objectives easier. After completing the reading assignment and completing the review exercises, you will be able to:

- Identify and draw the orientation tolerances.
- Complete orientation tolerance specifications including one or two datum references.
- Explain the effects of material condition modifiers when orientation tolerances are applied to features of size.
- Calculate the virtual condition for internal and external features of size to which an orientation tolerance is applied.
- Complete tolerance specifications that include orientation and form requirements on a single feature.

——————————————— REVIEW EXERCISES ———————————————

Place your answers in the spaces provided. Show all calculations for problems that require mathematical solutions.

MULTIPLE CHOICE

_____ 1. There must be _____ datum reference(s) in a perpendicularity tolerance specification.
  A. no
  B. one
  C. one or more
  D. two or more

_____ 2. Two _____ form the tolerance zone boundary when an orientation tolerance is applied to a flat surface.
  A. intersecting lines
  B. intersecting surfaces
  C. parallel lines
  D. parallel planes

_____ 3. _____ datum reference(s) may be necessary to obtain the desired level of control with an orientation tolerance.
  A. No
  B. One
  C. Two
  D. One or two

4. The _____ condition caused by an orientation tolerance applied to a hole is determined by subtracting the orientation tolerance from the minimum size limit of the hole.
   A. virtual
   B. resultant
   C. MMC
   D. LMC

5. A parallelism tolerance applied to a flat surface results in a tolerance zone that is bounded by _____ that are parallel to a referenced datum plane.
   A. lines
   B. planes
   C. cylinders
   D. None of the above.

6. Application of a parallelism tolerance on a hole requires that a _____ be assumed or applied on the tolerance value.
   A. minimum value
   B. maximum value
   C. metric value
   D. material condition modifier

7. A perpendicularity tolerance applied to a flat surface on the end of a rectangular part controls _____.
   A. only the surface to which it is applied
   B. both the surface to which it is applied and the opposite end of the part
   C. the center plane of the controlled feature of size
   D. None of the above.

8. A perpendicularity tolerance applied to the width dimension on a slot controls _____ to a value equal to the tolerance value.
   A. both sides of the slot
   B. the side of the slot closest to the tolerance specification
   C. the center plane created by the sides of the slot
   D. All of the above.

9. An orientation tolerance noted to apply to _____ may result in surface errors that lie outside the tolerance zone, but a plane tangent to the surface must be within the tolerance zone.
   A. an individual feature
   B. multiple features
   C. a unit area
   D. a tangent plane

TRUE/FALSE

10. Parallelism tolerances may only be applied to flat surfaces. (A)True or (B)False?

11. An orientation tolerance may be used to establish a location requirement. (A)True or (B)False?

12. An orientation tolerance should not be applied to a feature that is already controlled by another tolerance type such as a position tolerance. (A)True or (B)False?

13. An orientation tolerance applied to an internal feature of size, such as a hole, creates a virtual condition that is smaller than the MMC size of the controlled feature. (A)True or (B)False?

_____ 14. A parallelism tolerance controls orientation, and does not establish the maximum and minimum limits of size for a feature. (A)True or (B)False?

_____ 15. A parallelism tolerance of .008″ can be used to control the distance between two flat surfaces. (A)True or (B)False?

_____ 16. A diameter symbol is needed when a parallelism tolerance is applied to control the parallelism of one hole to the axis of another hole. (A)True or (B)False?

_____ 17. Ninety degree angles do not require dimensions to show the angle. (A)True or (B)False?

_____ 18. A perpendicularity tolerance must never reference two datums. (A)True or (B)False?

_____ 19. A secondary datum reference in a perpendicularity tolerance specification stops rotation of the part on the primary datum and, therefore, stabilizes the tolerance zone. (A)True or (B)False?

FILL IN THE BLANK

_____ 20. _____ tolerances are used to control parallelism and perpendicularity.

_____ 21. _____ is specified for control of any orientation other than parallel and perpendicular.

_____ 22. When no material condition modifier is shown on an orientation tolerance, the _____ material condition modifier is assumed to apply.

_____ 23. A parallelism tolerance value applied to a flat surface must not be _____ than the tolerance value that locates the surface.

_____ 24. The primary datum referenced in a perpendicularity tolerance specification must be at a _____ angle to the toleranced feature.

_____ 25. Surfaces controlled by an orientation tolerance must have a form that is equal to or _____ than the orientation tolerance.

_____ 26. An angularity tolerance specification applied to a flat surface results in a tolerance zone bounded by two _____.

_____ 27. The angle dimension value must be _____ when an angularity tolerance is applied.

SHORT ANSWER

28. List the three orientation tolerances. _____

_____

29. When is a material condition modifier applicable to an orientation tolerance? _____

_____

_____

30. Describe what is meant by the term "virtual condition" when the term is associated with a shaft.

_____

_____

31. How much parallelism error may exist when the dimension between two surfaces is ± .015″?

_____

32. Explain why it is possible to have a location tolerance of .050″ between two holes and a parallelism tolerance of .010″ between the same two holes. _____

_____

_____

_____

33. When is a 90° angle understood to be basic? _____

_____

_____

34. Determine the virtual condition for a .563″, plus .005″, minus .000″ diameter pin that has a .012″ diameter perpendicularity tolerance. _____

_____

35. Determine the virtual condition for a .750″, plus .006″, minus .002″ diameter hole that has a .010″ diameter perpendicularity tolerance. _____

_____

APPLICATION PROBLEMS

All application problems are to be completed using correct dimensioning techniques. Show any required calculations.

36. Show the tolerance zone for each of the inclined surfaces.

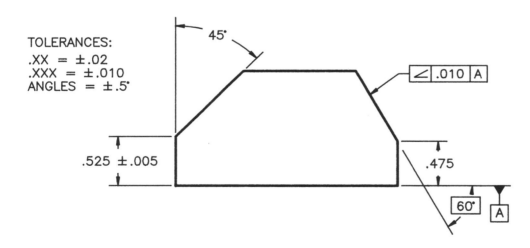

37. Identify each of the shown symbols.

∠   A. _____

⊥   B. _____

//   C. _____

38. Complete a feature control frame that controls a flat surface to be perpendicular to datum surface A within a zone that is .006″ wide.

39. Calculate the virtual condition for the shown hole.

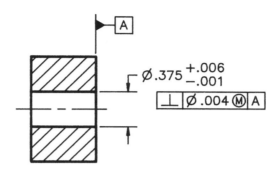

40. Calculate the virtual condition for the shown pin.

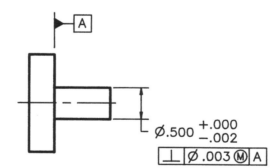

41. Surface B must be parallel within .005″ to a datum established by surface A. Surface C must be parallel within .010″ to the same datum. Show all required tolerance specifications.

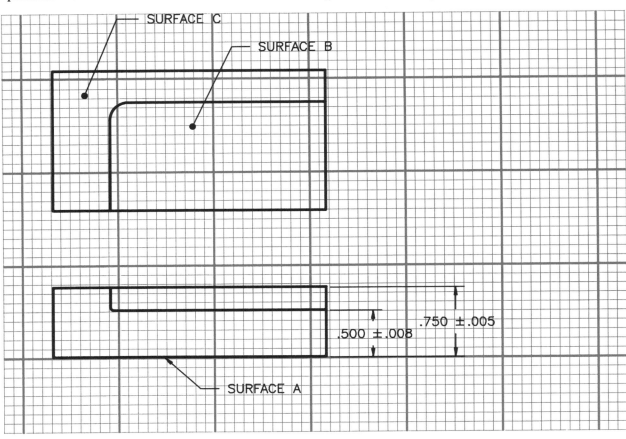

42. Complete the interpretation drawing and show the allowable tolerance zones for all specified tolerances.

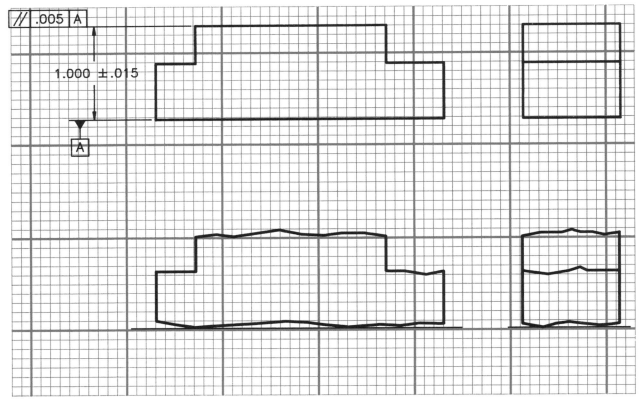

43. Apply a size dimension to permit the slot width to vary by .020″ total, and also control the sides of the slot to be parallel to one another within .008″.

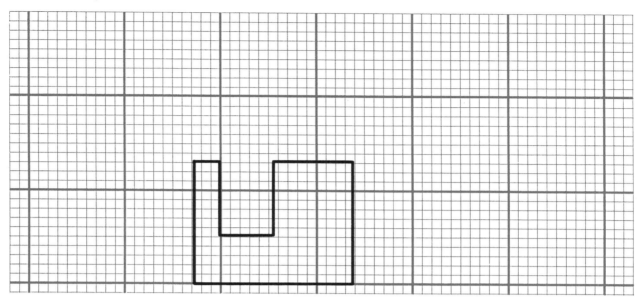

44. Apply a location tolerance of ± .025″ between the shown holes. Establish one hole as a datum feature. Control parallelism between the holes to .010″ when both holes are at MMC.

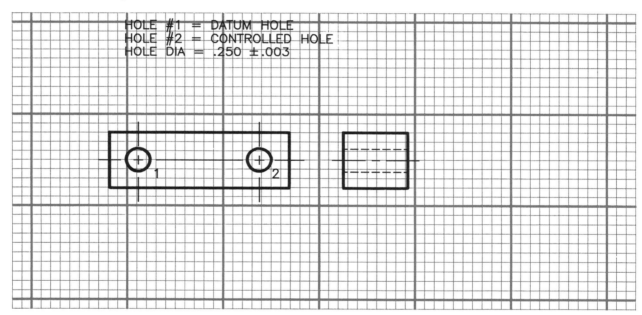

HOLE #1 = DATUM HOLE
HOLE #2 = CONTROLLED HOLE
HOLE DIA = .250 ±.003

45. Complete an interpretation drawing that shows the permitted perpendicularity tolerance zone.

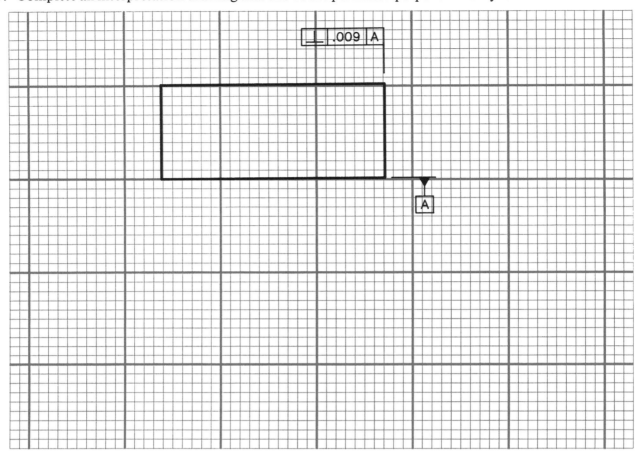

46. Complete an interpretation drawing that shows the permitted perpendicularity tolerance zone.

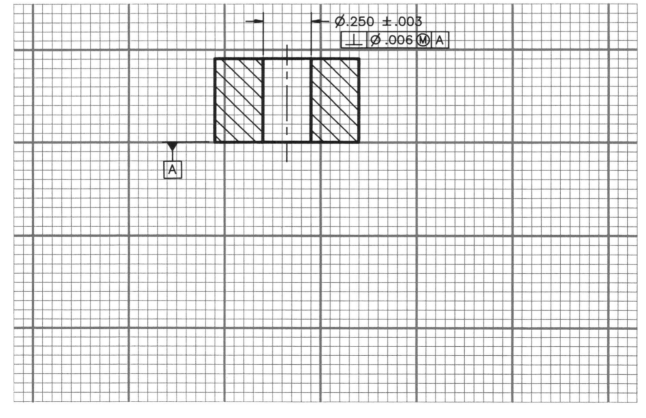

47. A hole size specification and perpendicularity tolerance is shown. Complete the given table to show each permitted hole size and show the corresponding allowable perpendicularity tolerances.

GIVEN HOLE
SPECIFICATION

$\varnothing.375 \begin{smallmatrix} +.004 \\ -.001 \end{smallmatrix}$

| ⊥ | ⌀ .007 Ⓜ | A |

PRODUCED HOLE DIAMETER	ALLOWABLE PERP. TOLERANCE
.374	
.375	
.376	
.377	
.378	
.379	

48. Apply a perpendicularity tolerance that results in a virtual condition of .379″ diameter for the pin.

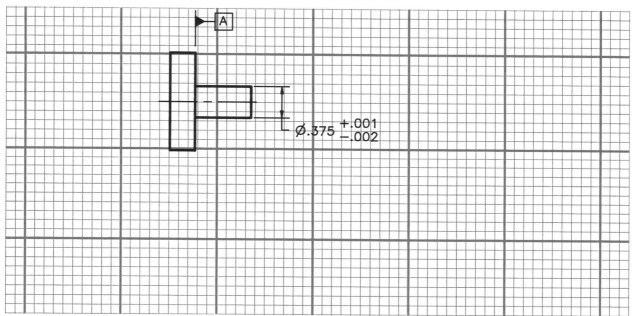

$\varnothing.375 \begin{smallmatrix} +.001 \\ -.002 \end{smallmatrix}$

49. Apply a perpendicularity tolerance that results in a virtual condition of .379″ diameter for the hole.

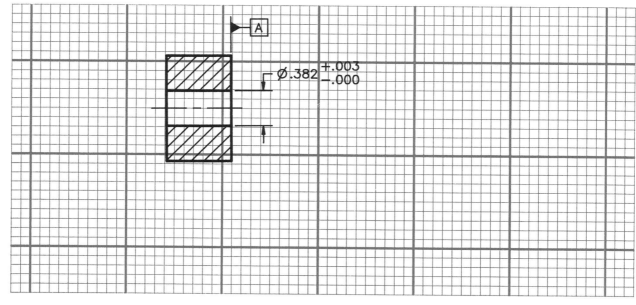

$\varnothing.382 \begin{smallmatrix} +.003 \\ -.000 \end{smallmatrix}$

50. Complete an interpretation drawing that shows the permitted angularity tolerance zone.

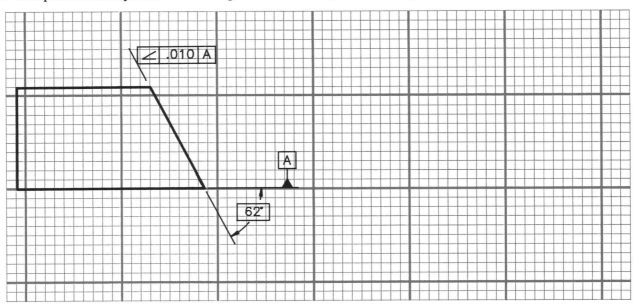

51. Complete an interpretation drawing that shows the permitted angularity tolerance zone. Show a permissible surface condition that lies partially outside the specified tolerance zone.

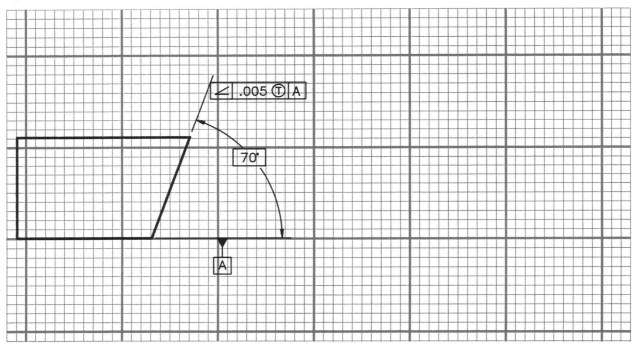

52. Complete a feature control frame that controls parallelism of the top surface to .015″ relative to datum A and flatness to .005″.

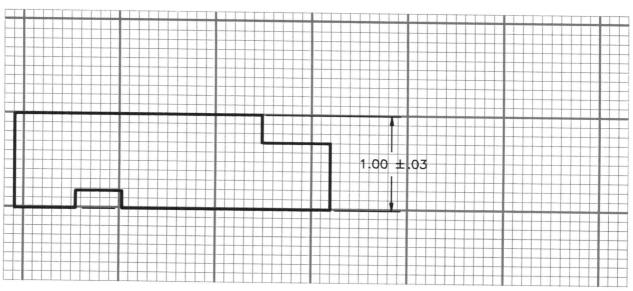

53. Complete a feature control frame that controls perpendicularity of the hole to .012″ at MMC relative to datum A and axis straightness to .004″ at MMC.

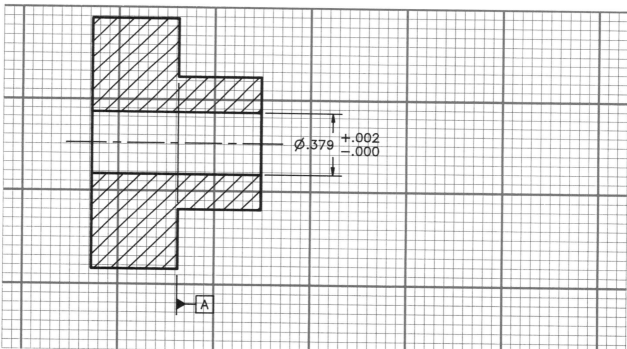

Chapter 8

POSITION TOLERANCING–FUNDAMENTALS

READING

Read Chapter 8 of the *Design Dimensioning and Tolerancing* textbook prior to completing the review exercises.

OBJECTIVES

A combination of activities is required to achieve the following objectives. Completing the reading assignment and the following review exercises are an important part of achieving the objectives. Familiarization with the objectives prior to completion of the reading assignment and review exercises will make mastery of the objectives easier. After completing the reading assignment and completing the review exercises, you will be able to:

- Complete feature control frames for position tolerances, properly using the diameter symbol, material condition modifiers, and datum references.
- Sketch the proper location and shape for position tolerance zones.
- Describe the effect of an MMC, LMC, or RFS modifier on a position tolerance.
- Provide examples that prove the validity of the MMC concept as it applies to position tolerances.
- Calculate position tolerances for simple fixed and floating fastener conditions.
- Calculate the allowable bonus tolerance for a produced part on which a position tolerance is specified at MMC.
- Use paper gaging techniques to verify whether produced hole locations meet specified drawing tolerances.
- Cite advantages of position tolerances when compared to coordinate hole location tolerances.

————————————— REVIEW EXERCISES —————————————

Place your answers in the spaces provided. Accurately complete any required sketches. Show all calculations for problems that require mathematical solutions.

MULTIPLE CHOICE

_____ 1. Location dimensions must be _____ if a position tolerance is applied to the located feature.
   A. nominal values
   B. limit values
   C. toleranced
   D. basic

_____ 2. Application of position tolerances for hole locations requires that datum _____ be identified on the part.
   A. features
   B. planes
   C. axes
   D. None of the above.

_____ 3. The 1982 and later issues of the dimensioning and tolerancing standard prohibit _____ on position tolerances.
   A. implied datums
   B. the use of MMC
   C. Both A and B.
   D. Neither A nor B.

_____ 4. Rule #2 requires that material condition modifiers be shown on position tolerances when _____ applies.
   A. MMC
   B. LMC
   C. RFS
   D. Either A or B.

_____ 5. A position tolerance zone for a round hole is normally _____ in geometric shape.
   A. conical
   B. cylindrical
   C. circular
   D. square

_____ 6. The _____ modifier indicates that a tolerance may increase as a hole size departs from the minimum permitted diameter.
   A. MMC
   B. LMC
   C. RFS
   D. None of the above.

_____ 7. If two mating parts each have clearance holes through which a bolt is inserted, a _____ condition exists.
   A. slip fit
   B. floating fastener
   C. running/sliding
   D. fixed fastener

_____ 8. Fastener and clearance hole _____ are used to calculate position tolerances.
   A. nominal sizes
   B. maximum size limits
   C. least material conditions
   D. maximum material conditions

_____ 9. Specification of a position tolerance with a MMC modifier results in a(n) _____ tolerance when the feature is produced at any allowable size other than MMC.
   A. undefined
   B. bonus
   C. reduced
   D. None of the above.

_____ 10. The allowable position tolerance is equal to the sum of the _____ and the bonus tolerance.
   A. specified tolerance
   B. feature size tolerance
   C. specified feature size
   D. actual produced diameter

_____ 11. Specified hole limits of .384″ MIN and .394″ MAX are given. A position tolerance of .009″ diameter at MMC is specified for the hole. What is the allowable position tolerance for a hole produced at .386″ diameter?
  A. .007″
  B. .009″
  C. .011″
  D. .015″

_____ 12. A position tolerance referenced to three datum planes requires that all hole locations be measured from _____.
  A. the datum planes
  B. the datum features
  C. one another
  D. with a coordinate measurement machine

_____ 13. _____-shaped position tolerance zones permit the same amount of hole location error in all directions.
  A. Round
  B. Square
  C. Rectangular
  D. None of the above.

_____ 14. A position tolerance applied to a thread controls the location of the _____ diameter.
  A. major
  B. pitch
  C. minor
  D. root

_____ 15. A _____ tolerance zone lies outside the controlled feature.
  A. projected
  B. position
  C. runout
  D. bonus

_____ 16. _____ feature control frames can be applied to a feature of size to specify a larger allowable position tolerance in one direction than is permitted in the other direction.
  A. Two
  B. Composite
  C. Combined
  D. None of the above.

_____ 17. A position tolerance applied to control the location of a slot requires that _____ of the slot be located within the allowable tolerance.
  A. one side
  B. both sides
  C. the center plane
  D. All of the above.

TRUE/FALSE

_____ 18. Position tolerances are applied only to features of size. (A)True or (B)False?

_____ 19. Every position tolerance specification must include a material condition modifier on the tolerance value. (A)True or (B)False?

_____ 20. Issues of ANSI Y14.5M prior to 1982 permitted implied datums on position tolerance specifications. (A)True or (B)False?

_____ 21. It is necessary to show a material condition modifier on a datum reference in a position tolerance specification if the datum feature is a feature
of size. (A)True or (B)False?

_____ 22. The theoretical true position for a hole defines the exact location at which
a produced hole must be located. (A)True or (B)False?

_____ 23. The allowable tolerance zone is dependent on the amount of hole size
departure from MMC if the RFS modifier is applied to the position tolerance specification. (A)True or (B)False?

_____ 24. An MMC modifier on a position tolerance can permit greater freedom in
how a part is produced. (A)True or (B)False?

_____ 25. T = H - F is a simple formula that can be used for a floating fastener
condition in which both holes are the same size and the position tolerance
applied to each hole is the same value. (A)True or (B)False?

_____ 26. If an MMC modifier is applied to a position tolerance on a hole, the
tolerance increases as the hole size is increased. (A)True or (B)False?

_____ 27. Functional gages must be used to verify hole positions when position
tolerances are specified. (A)True or (B)False?

_____ 28. Position tolerances permit utilization of the full amount of tolerance that
is functionally possible for a hole, but coordinate tolerances do not.
(A)True or (B)False?

_____ 29. Position tolerances are not appropriate or needed when the allowable
variation is relatively large. (A)True or (B)False?

_____ 30. Square tolerance zones do not permit the same amount of permissible
hole location error in all directions. (A)True or (B)False?

_____ 31. Bonus tolerances may be utilized when coordinate tolerances are applied
to hole locations. (A)True or (B)False?

FILL IN THE BLANK

_____ 32. A(n) _____ symbol placed in front of the position tolerance value
indicates the tolerance zone is round.

_____ 33. Position tolerance zones are centered on the _____ position defined by basic dimensions.

_____ 34. A hole for a press fit pin would typically have a position tolerance that
applies at the _____ material condition.

_____ 35. A large amount of clearance between a hole and fastener permits
_____ position tolerance than would be possible for a small amount
of clearance.

_____ 36. The use of the _____ material condition results in no allowable
change in the specified tolerance regardless of the produced feature size.

_____ 37. Concentric circles superimposed on a grid can be used to represent
_____ zone diameters when paper gaging.

_____ 38. A round tolerance zone has _____ percent more area than a square
tolerance zone if the effect of bonus tolerances is ignored.

_____ 39. The letter P inside a circle indicates a requirement for a _____
tolerance zone.

SHORT ANSWER

40. Why is it necessary to permit tolerances on the location of features? _____
_____
_____
_____

41. Describe one method that can be used to show the number of holes to which a position tolerance applies. _____
_____
_____
_____

42. Describe one reason why implied datums shouldn't be used, even when working to an old issue of the standard. _____
_____
_____
_____

43. List the two general fastener conditions for which position tolerances may be calculated.
_____
_____

44. Describe a fixed fastener condition. _____
_____
_____

45. What is the formula used to calculate the position tolerance for a fixed fastener condition? Assume even distribution of the allowable tolerance for the two parts. _____
_____

46. Coordinates specified for a hole are: X = 1.375″ and Y = 3.250″. A hole is produced at X = 1.381″ and Y = 3.248″. What is the diameter of position error? Show your calculations. _____
_____
_____
_____

47. Explain why a functionally correct round tolerance zone has a diameter that circumscribes a calculated square tolerance zone. _____
_____
_____
_____

48. What is the effect on the hole and counterbore when a single position tolerance specification is applied to the hole and counterbore callout? _____

_____

_____

49. Explain an advantage of bidirectional position tolerances applied at MMC as compared to plus or minus location tolerances on a hole. _____

_____

_____

_____

APPLICATION PROBLEMS

All application problems are to be completed using correct dimensioning techniques. Show any required calculations.

50. Identify a basic dimension, a datum feature symbol, and a position tolerance specification.

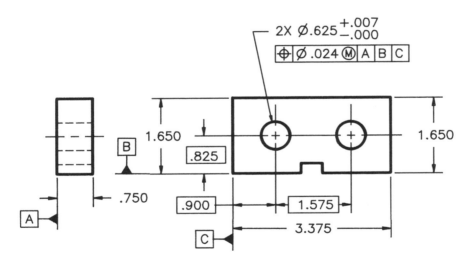

51. Complete a feature control frame for a position tolerance that is related to primary datum A, secondary datum C, and tertiary datum F. The tolerance zone is to be .024″ diameter regardless of feature size.

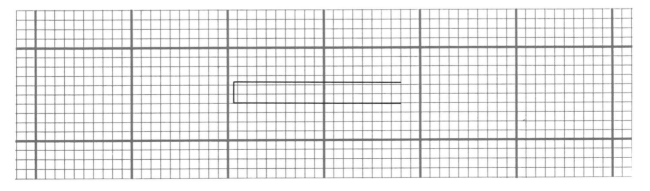

52. Complete a feature control frame for a position tolerance that is related to primary datum D, secondary datum C, and tertiary datum G. The tolerance zone is to be .031″ diameter when the feature is at maximum material condition.

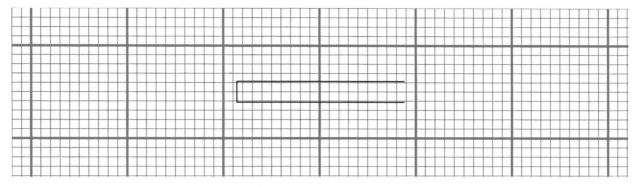

53. Draw the shown tolerance specification in an acceptable location that indicates the tolerance applies to all four holes. Make the necessary dimensions basic.

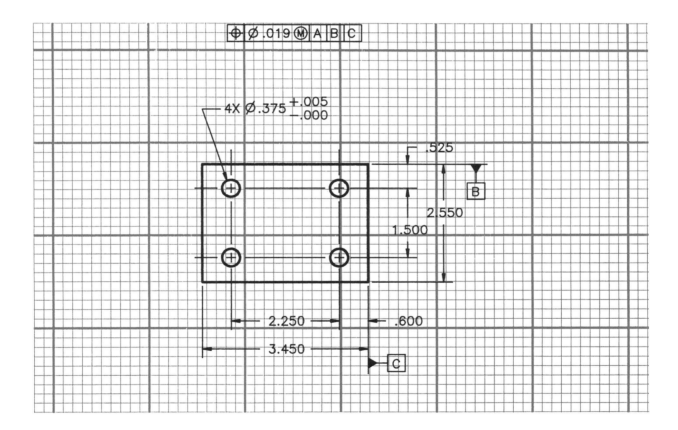

54. Two drawings of similar parts are given. Below each drawing is a figure of a part produced to the drawing. Assume the holes are produced exactly on the true positions defined in the drawing. Show dimensions on the produced parts to indicate how the location dimensions are measured on each of the given parts. Show any datum planes that may be needed.

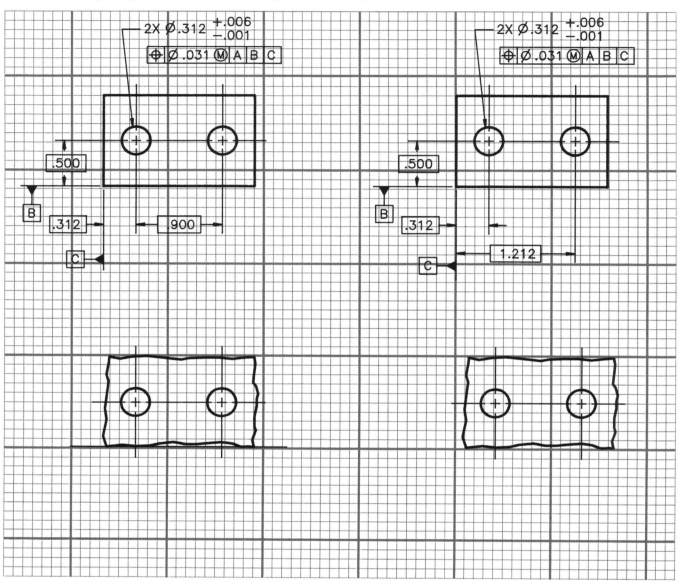

55. Complete calculations to determine the allowable position tolerance for each of the applications shown in the table. Each of the applications is for a floating fastener. Insert your answers in the given table.

SPECIFIED HOLE DIA	FASTENER DIA AT MMC	ALLOWABLE POSITION TOLERANCE AT MMC
.221 ±.003	.190	
.219 ±.002	.190	
.282 ±.004	.250	

56. Complete the given table. All problems are for a floating fastener application.

HOLE DIA AT MMC	FASTENER DIA AT MMC	ALLOWABLE POSITION TOLERANCE AT MMC
.189	.164	
	.190	.031
.279		.029

57. Complete the given table. All problems are for a fixed fastener application.

CLEARANCE HOLE DIA AT MMC	FASTENER DIA AT MMC	ALLOWABLE POSITION TOLERANCE AT MMC
.282	.250	.016
.218	.190	.014
.354	.312	.021

58. Determine the X and Y errors for each produced hole and plot the hole locations on the given grid. Label each hole location with the hole identification number. Draw circles to represent tolerance zone diameters. Note each hole location as acceptable or unacceptable. Each grid space equals .001″.

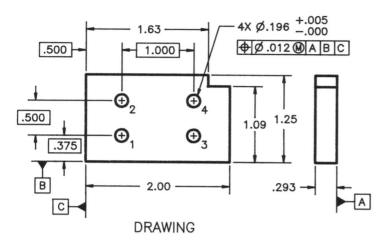

DRAWING

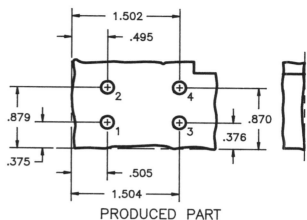

PRODUCED PART

Hole #	1		2	
Diameter	.199		.201	
	X	Y	X	Y
Measured Location				
Drawing Dimension	.500	.375	.500	.875
Error				

Hole #	3		4	
Diameter	.200		.200	
	X	Y	X	Y
Measured Location				
Drawing Dimension	1.500	.375	1.500	.875
Error				

MEASURED HOLE DATA

PLOTTED COORDINATE
ERRORS AND
POSITION TOLERANCE ZONES

59. Complete the hole specification including a position tolerance of .018″ diameter at MMC relative to primary datum A, secondary datum B, and tertiary datum C. Apply the tolerance specification in such a manner that both the hole and counterbore are controlled.

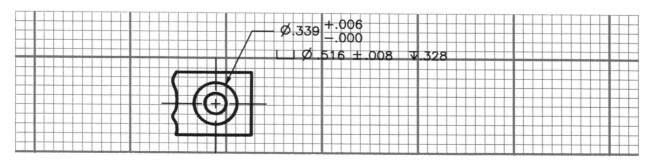

60. Redraw the feature control frame to specify a projected tolerance zone that extends .375″.

$$\boxed{\oplus}\ \boxed{\varnothing .024\ \text{\textcircled{M}}}\ \boxed{A}\ \boxed{B}\ \boxed{C}$$

61. Apply a position tolerance on the given slot to permit .045″ location error in the X axis and a .015″ in the Y axis.

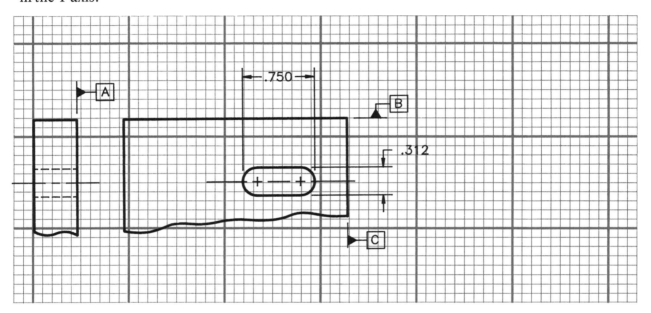

62. Complete the detail drawings of the two given parts to the extent required to define hole location requirements. Select and identify datums. Dimension hole locations. Dimension hole diameters, including size tolerances. Calculate and apply position tolerances that ensure the two parts can be assembled.

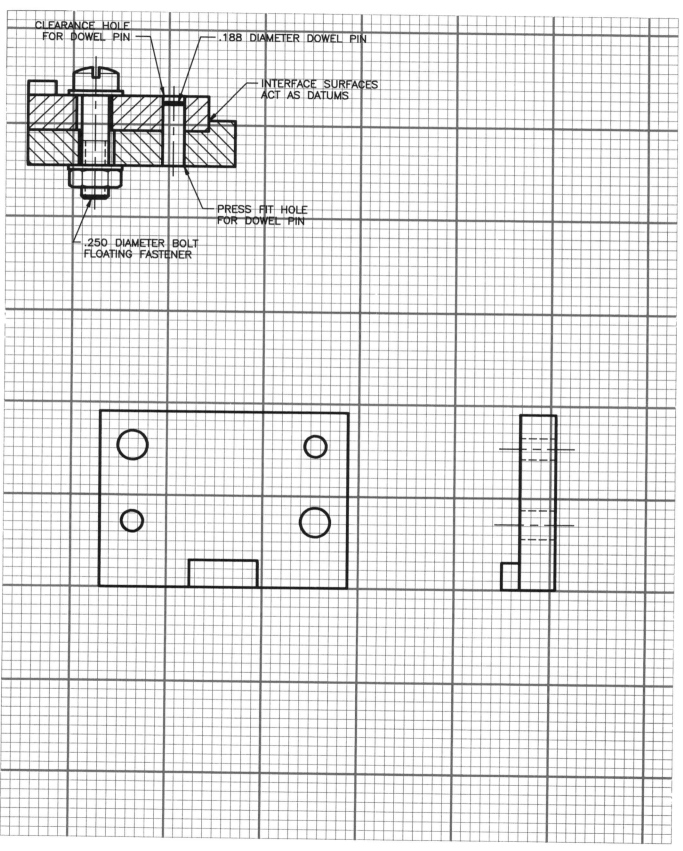

CLEARANCE HOLE FOR DOWEL PIN

.188 DIAMETER DOWEL PIN

INTERFACE SURFACES ACT AS DATUMS

PRESS FIT HOLE FOR DOWEL PIN

.250 DIAMETER BOLT FLOATING FASTENER

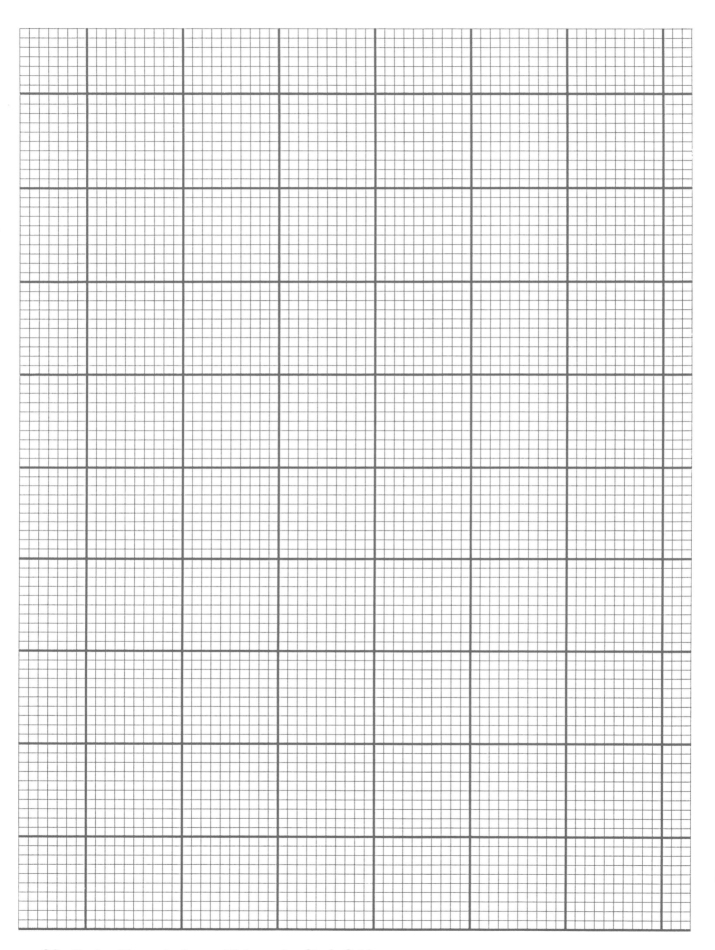

Chapter 9

POSITION TOLERANCES–EXPANDED PRINCIPLES, SYMMETRY, AND CONCENTRICITY

READING

Read Chapter 9 of the *Design Dimensioning and Tolerancing* textbook prior to completing the review exercises.

OBJECTIVES

A combination of activities is required to achieve the following objectives. Completing the reading assignment and the following review exercises are an important part of achieving the objectives. Familiarization with the objectives prior to completion of the reading assignment and review exercises will make mastery of the objectives easier. After completing the reading assignment and completing the review exercises, you will be able to:
- Explain functional gaging methods for checking hole position tolerances specified at MMC.
- Specify and explain composite position tolerance specifications.
- Explain the effect of using identical datum references in multiple position tolerance specifications.
- Specify separate pattern requirements for groups of features not acting as a single pattern.
- Specify position tolerances for in-line holes.
- Specify tolerances to control symmetry.
- Control coaxial features with position or concentricity tolerances, depending on the given application.
- Interpret position tolerances created in compliance with the previous issue of the dimensioning and tolerancing standard.

─────────────────── REVIEW EXERCISES ───────────────────

Place your answers in the spaces provided. Show all calculations for problems that require mathematical solutions.

MULTIPLE CHOICE

_____ 1. A single line position tolerance specification establishes tolerance zones that have _____ relative to the referenced datums.
  A. fixed positions
  B. no location requirement
  C. only a fixed orientation
  D. no orientation requirement

_____ 2. A pattern locating tolerance is specified _____ the feature relating tolerance.
  A. above
  B. below
  C. either above or below
  D. in a separate feature control frame than

3. The feature relating tolerance is always _____ than the pattern locating tolerance in a composite position tolerance specification.
   A. smaller
   B. larger
   C. equal to or less
   D. equal to or greater

4. Referencing primary and secondary datum surfaces in the second line of a composite tolerance specification requires control of orientation to the datums but does not require _____ relative to the datums.
   A. part verification
   B. angularity
   C. location
   D. None of the above.

5. No _____ is created when two position tolerance symbols are shown in a two line feature control frame.
   A. valid specification
   B. position tolerance specification
   C. composite tolerance specification
   D. All of the above.

6. The complexity of a functional gage may be impacted by the number of _____.
   A. features being checked
   B. tolerance controls placed on the features
   C. referenced datums
   D. All of the above.

7. An MMC modifier on a _____ datum reference requires the virtual condition of the datum feature to be used to establish the datum location.
   A. primary or secondary
   B. secondary or tertiary
   C. primary or tertiary
   D. All of the above.

8. The primary characteristic on a drawing that determines whether all holes belong to one or more patterns is the _____.
   A. datum references in the position tolerance specifications
   B. grouping of holes
   C. hole size
   D. manner in which hole location dimensions are applied

9. Coaxial (or in-line) holes _____ when using a position tolerance to specify a tolerance that controls the in-line condition.
   A. must be the same diameter
   B. may be different diameters
   C. must have one hole referenced as a datum
   D. None of the above.

10. _____ tolerances should only be used when it is necessary to control one axis relative to another.
    A. Position
    B. Concentricity
    C. Runout
    D. Composite position

Name _____ **Date** _____

TRUE/FALSE

_____ 11. Parts inspection may be simplified by using functional gages to check position tolerances instead of paper gaging large quantities of parts. (A)True or (B)False?

_____ 12. In composite position tolerances, the feature relating tolerance controls feature-to-feature positions. (A)True or (B)False?

_____ 13. All of a feature relating tolerance zone must be contained within a pattern locating tolerance zone. (A)True or (B)False?

_____ 14. A feature relating tolerance zone framework must be properly oriented relative to the primary datum that is referenced in the second line of a composite position tolerance specification. (A)True or (B)False?

_____ 15. If the first set of location measurements for a pattern of holes do not meet the feature relating tolerance specification, different holes within the pattern may be used to establish a coordinate system for an improved set of measurements. (A)True or (B)False?

_____ 16. Two position tolerance symbols may be used in a two line feature control frame to specify a composite tolerance. (A)True or (B)False?

_____ 17. A functional gage containing a pin sized to the virtual condition of a hole automatically checks the hole location and the hole size. (A)True or (B)False?

_____ 18. Any reference to a datum feature of size must include the MMC material condition modifier when included in a position tolerance. (A)True or (B)False?

_____ 19. The two gages used to check the pattern locating tolerance and the feature relating tolerance for a pattern of holes both have the same diameter of gage pins. (A)True or (B)False?

_____ 20. All holes are known to act as a single pattern if the holes are all one diameter. (A)True or (B)False?

_____ 21. A composite position tolerance, instead of concentricity, applied to two or more coaxial (in-line) holes must contain at least one datum reference for the feature relating tolerance. (A)True or (B)False?

_____ 22. Position tolerances are typically applied to coaxial parts when the main concern is assembly of the parts. (A)True or (B)False?

_____ 23. Symmetry tolerances should not be applied to any features other than hole patterns. (A)True or (B)False?

_____ 24. Concentricity tolerances can be used to control the surface conditions of one cylinder relative to another. (A)True or (B)False?

FILL IN THE BLANK

_____ 25. A single line position tolerance specification controls hole locations within _____ tolerance value that applies to each hole.

_____ 26. In composite position tolerances, the _____ locating tolerance controls the hole pattern positions relative to the datum references frame.

_____ 27. The _____ line of a composite position tolerance always specifies the pattern locating tolerance.

_____ 28. The _____ line of a composite position tolerance has the same effect as a single line position tolerance specification.

_____ 29. Paper gaging the feature relating tolerance for a pattern of holes requires that one _____ be used as the origin for measurements.

_____ 30. A functional gage for verifying hole locations automatically permits utilization of any allowable bonus tolerance since gage pins are sized to the _____ of the holes being checked.

_____ 31. An MMC modifier on a primary datum reference requires the _____ size of the datum feature be used to establish the datum location.

_____ 32. Placing the words _____ under a position tolerance specification results in the associated group of holes acting as a separate pattern from any other holes or features.

_____ 33. If two groups of holes are controlled with composite position tolerances that reference different datums, _____ patterns of features are created.

_____ 34. Symmetry tolerances are specified using the _____ symbol when a drawing is in compliance with the 1982 standard.

_____ 35. Concentricity is always specified with the _____ modifier.

SHORT ANSWER

36. What requirements apply to the specification of datums in the second line of a composite position tolerance? _____

_____

_____

37. Explain the feature relating tolerance zone framework requirement when no datum reference is shown in the second line of a composite position tolerance specification that is applied to a pattern of holes.

_____

_____

_____

_____

38. Why must two holes in a hole pattern be used to establish a coordinate system when making measurements to check the feature relating tolerances? _____

_____

_____

_____

39. What is a functional gage? _____

_____

_____

_____

40. What must be accomplished with the datum simulator if the outside diameter of a shaft is referenced as a datum feature with the RFS modifier applied to the reference? _____

_____

_____

_____

41. When features are dimensioned and toleranced according to the current standard, what indicates that features belong to a single pattern? _____

_____

_____

_____

_____

42. Why is it possible to dimension a hole pattern without showing a dimension from the pattern of holes to a datum feature when a symmetry position tolerance is specified? _____

_____

_____

43. What tolerance types are preferable to concentricity for controlling coaxial features?

_____

_____

_____

_____

44. When implied datums were used on a pre-1982 position tolerance specification, what was the risk related to how datums might be assumed in machining and inspection of the part?

_____

_____

_____

APPLICATION PROBLEMS

All application problems are to be completed using correct dimensioning techniques. Show any required calculations.

45. Complete a composite position tolerance specification that creates a pattern locating tolerance of .036″ diameter at MMC relative to datums A primary, B secondary, and C tertiary, and a feature relating tolerance of .011″ diameter at MMC relative to primary datum A.

46. Complete the given tolerance specification and identify the two lines of the feature control frame.

47. The pattern locating tolerance zone framework and the pattern locating tolerances are shown on the illustrated part. Show one possible location of the feature relating tolerance zone framework that does not coincide with the pattern locating tolerance zone framework. Also show the feature relating tolerance zones. Show one permissible point for the location of each hole.

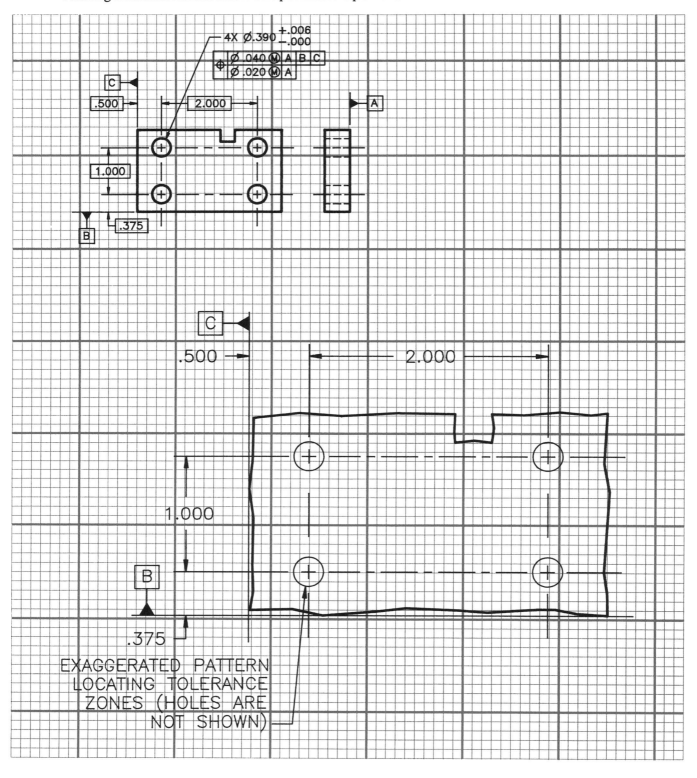

48. The pattern locating tolerance zone framework and the pattern locating tolerances are shown on the given part. Show one possible location of the feature relating tolerance zone framework that does not coincide with the pattern locating tolerance zone framework.

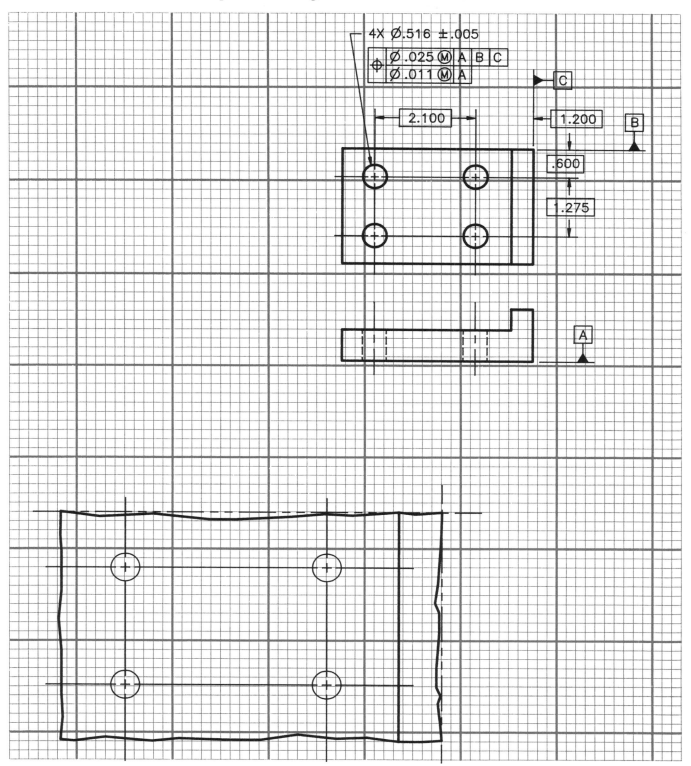

49. Complete all steps necessary to prove acceptability or rejection of the given part using paper gaging techniques. Verify only the feature relating tolerance.

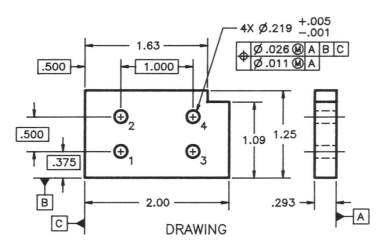

DRAWING

HOLE—TO—HOLE LOCATION ERRORS

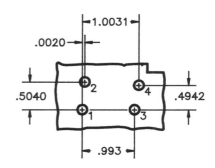

Hole #	1		2		3		4	
Diameter	.222		.223		.221		.223	
	X	Y	X	Y	X	Y	X	Y
Measured Location	0	0	.0020	.5040	.9930	0	1.0031	.4942
Drawing Dimension	0	0	0	.500	1.000	0	1.000	.500
Error								

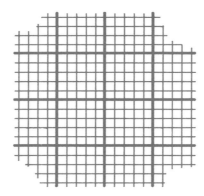

HOLE—TO—HOLE RELATIVE POSITIONS

50. Design a functional gage that checks the hole positions in the given part. Do not apply gage tolerances. Superimpose the gage on the given part where the part is shown with phantom lines.

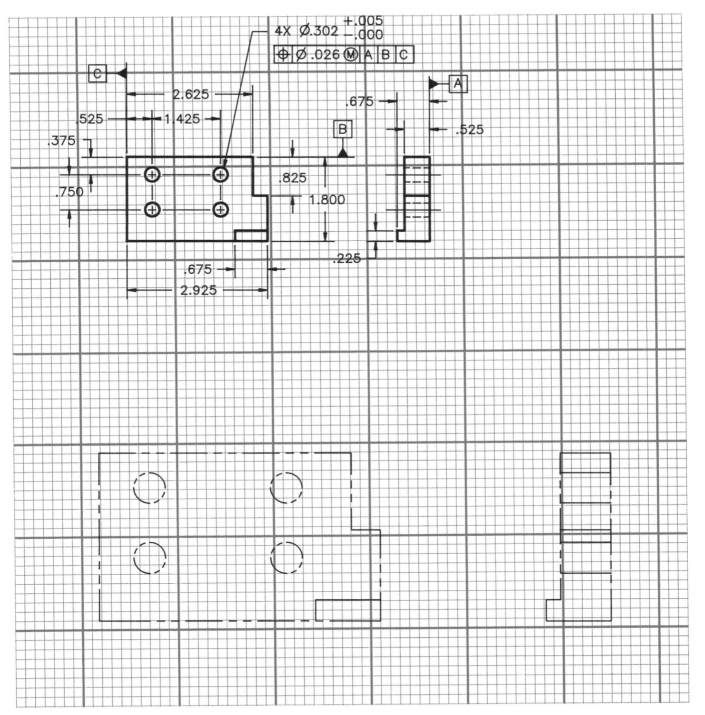

51. Calculate the diameter of a pin that establishes the secondary datum for the shown position tolerance specifications.

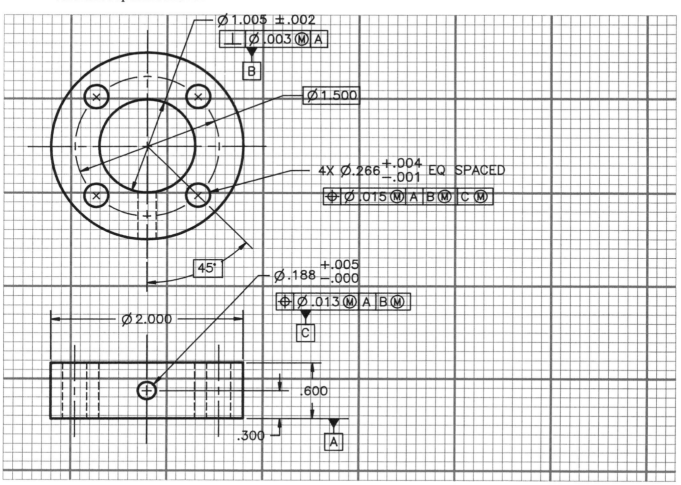

Name _____   **Date** _____

52. Complete a drawing of the gage(s) needed to verify the feature relating tolerance for all the holes in the given part.

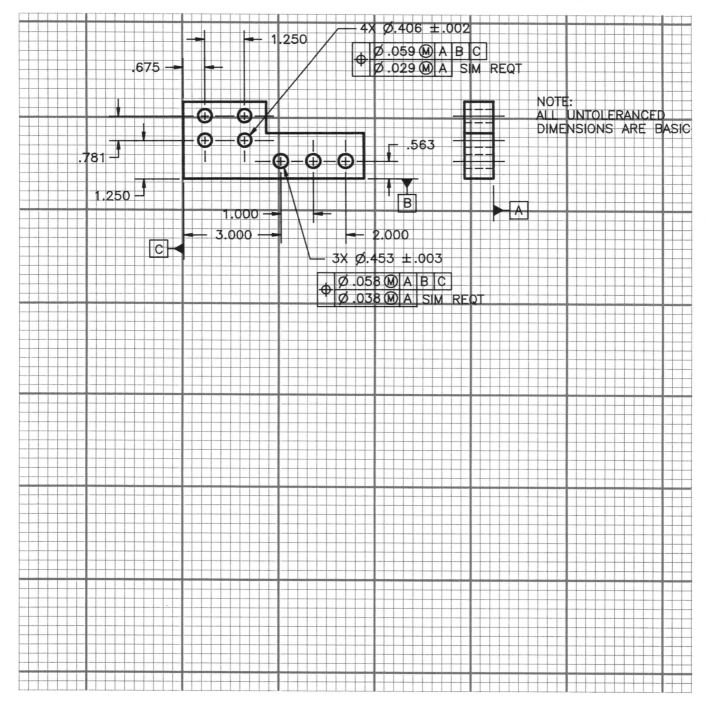

53. Complete a drawing of the gage(s) needed to verify the feature relating tolerance for all the holes in the given part.

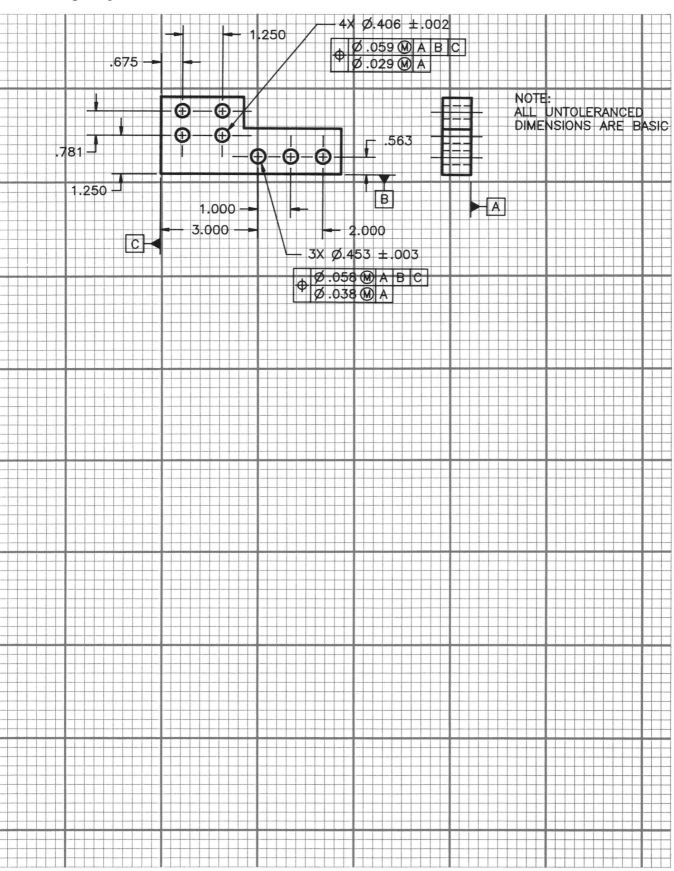

54. Apply a composite tolerance to permit a .1875″ plus or minus .0010″ diameter shaft to pass through the holes. The shaft must be located within .025″ diameter at MMC relative to datum A primary, B secondary, and C tertiary.

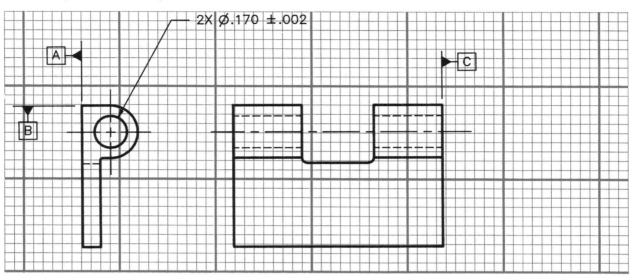

55. Sketch a simple gage that verifies the shown position tolerance.

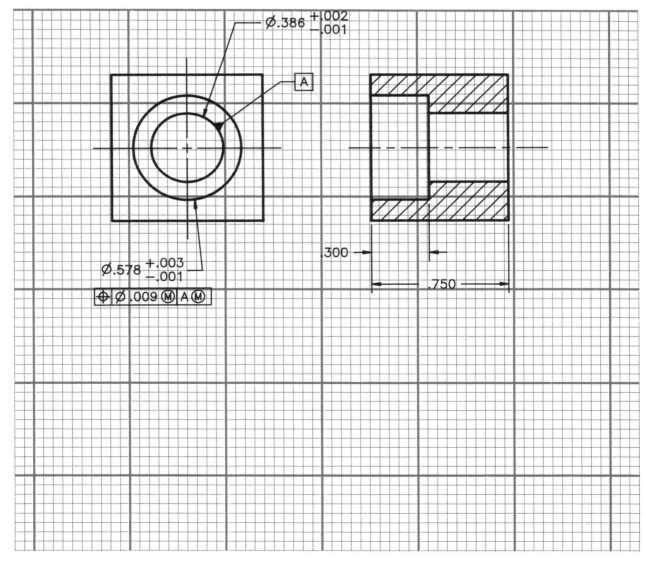

56. Apply any additional dimensions and tolerances needed to define hole locations that are symmetrically located to the slot within a .026″ diameter zone when the holes and slot are at MMC. Datum A is primary, the slot secondary, and one end of the part tertiary.

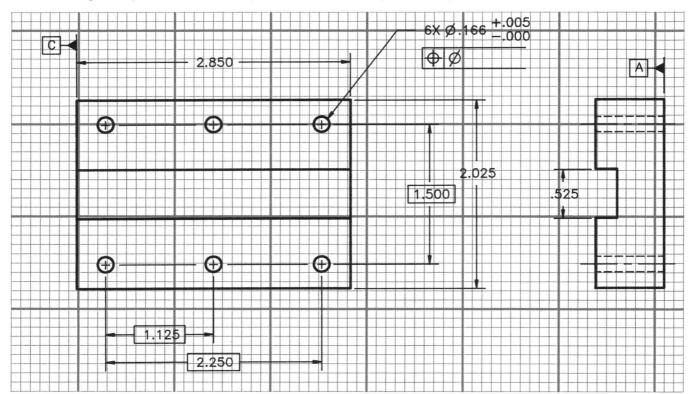

Chapter 10

RUNOUT

READING

Read Chapter 10 of the *Design Dimensioning and Tolerancing* textbook prior to completing the review exercises.

OBJECTIVES

A combination of activities is required to achieve the following objectives. Completing the reading assignment and the following review exercises are an important part of achieving the objectives. Familiarization with the objectives prior to completion of the reading assignment and review exercises will make mastery of the objectives easier. After completing the reading assignment and completing the review exercises, you will be able to:
- Describe the two types of runout tolerances.
- Complete an interpretation drawing showing how each of the runout tolerances are measured.
- Apply both types of runout tolerances on circular features and face surfaces.
- Specify runout tolerances using compound datum references.
- Limit the area of application for a runout tolerance.

———————————————————— REVIEW EXERCISES ————————————————————

Place your answers in the spaces provided. Show all calculations for problems that require mathematical solutions.

MULTIPLE CHOICE

_____ 1. _____ runout includes the error across an entire surface.
   A. Cylindrical
   B. Total
   C. Face surface
   D. Circular

_____ 2. Circular runout may be measured on any _____ that has circular elements.
   A. cone
   B. cylinder
   C. flat surface
   D. All of the above.

_____ 3. A circular runout symbol has _____ arrow(s).
   A. one
   B. two
   C. either one or two
   D. None of the above.

_____ 4. The modifier that always applies to runout tolerances is _____.
   A. MMC
   B. LMC
   C. RFS
   D. Any of the above.

_____ 5. Runout tolerance specifications must include a _____.
   A. datum reference
   B. MMC or LMC modifier
   C. three place decimal tolerance value
   D. None of the above.

_____ 6. Datum reference B-C indicates _____.
   A. one datum created by two datum features
   B. two datums created by two datum features
   C. a primary and secondary datum
   D. a single datum created by one datum feature that is identified with the letters B and C

_____ 7. A(n) _____ line may be used to indicate a limited area of application for a tolerance specification.
   A. object
   B. center
   C. phantom
   D. chain

TRUE/FALSE

_____ 8. Runout may only occur on a cylindrical surface. (A)True or (B)False?

_____ 9. One runout reading taken at a cross section on a 3.00″ long shaft is adequate to verify a circular runout specification for the 3.00″ shaft. (A)True or (B)False?

_____ 10. Runout tolerances applied to internal features require notations to explain what the specification means. (A)True or (B)False?

_____ 11. One datum reference is all that is ever needed for any runout tolerance specification. (A)True or (B)False?

_____ 12. A runout tolerance should not exceed the size tolerance on the controlled feature. (A)True or (B)False?

FILL IN THE BLANK

_____ 13. Runout is the amount of _____ variation that is allowed relative to an axis of rotation.

_____ 14. A part being inspected for runout error must be _____ on an axis to make the runout measurements.

_____ 15. Two features acting together to establish a single datum axis through them are referred to as _____ datum features.

_____ 16. Runout tolerances applied to the pitch diameter of a gear are measured by rolling the workpiece against a _____ gear.

_____ 17. A primary and secondary datum reference in a runout tolerance specification usually includes one _____ surface and one face (flat) surface.

_____ 18. _____ runout is the variation across an entire surface relative to an axis of rotation.

SHORT ANSWER

19. Explain how a circular runout requirement is checked on a cylindrical feature. _____

_____

_____

_____

20. Why isn't a diameter symbol used in runout tolerance specifications? _____

_____

_____

21. What is achieved by the application of a total runout tolerance on a surface that is perpendicular to the datum axis? _____

_____

_____

_____

22. Give one reason why there might be a datum reference such as D-E in a runout tolerance.

_____

_____

_____

_____

23. How may a face surface, as a secondary datum reference, be beneficial when a runout tolerance is referenced to a primary datum axis? _____

_____

_____

_____

24. List two geometric shapes that may be controlled with circular runout but not with total runout.

_____

APPLICATION PROBLEMS

All application problems are to be completed using correct dimensioning techniques. Show any required calculations.

25. Show three ways to apply a circular runout tolerance specification of .006″ on the small diameter relative to datum axis A.

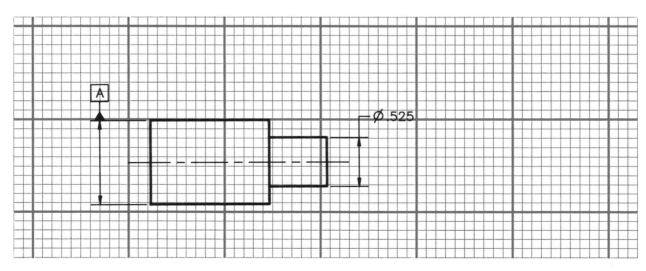

26. Sketch a setup and measurement method that may be used to check the runout tolerance. Also show the acceptable tolerance zone.

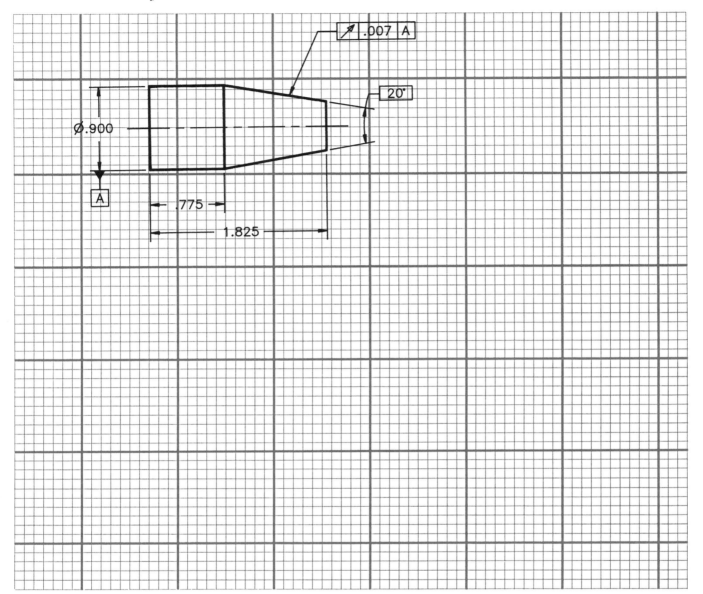

27. Complete a feature control frame that specifies a circular runout tolerance of .008″ relative to an axis established by datum feature C.

28. Sketch a setup and measurement method that may be used to check the runout tolerance. Also show the acceptable tolerance zone.

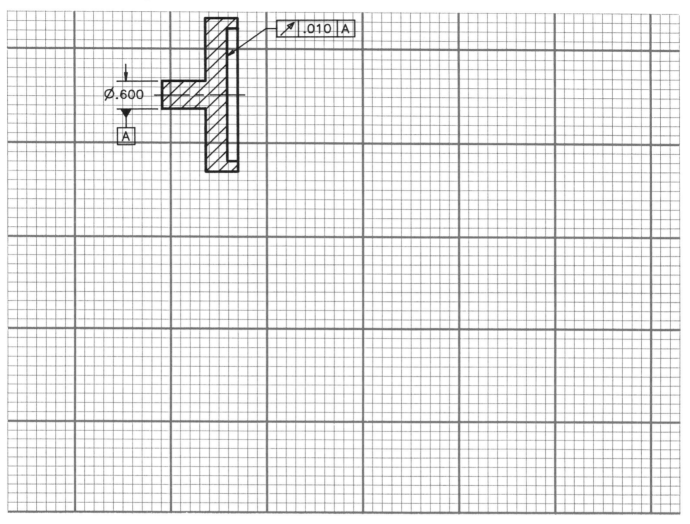

29. Apply the necessary symbology to control the circular runout of the .375″ diameter to a value of .006″ relative to an axis established by the two .250″ diameter bearing surfaces.

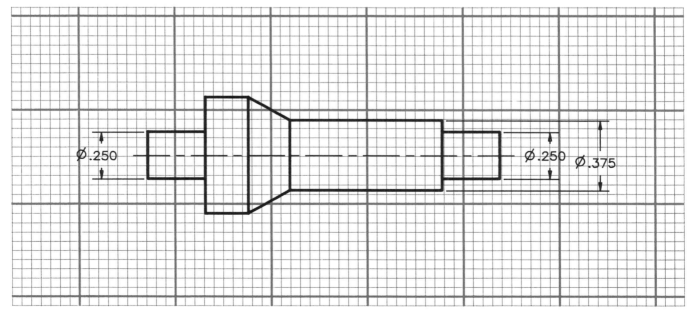

30. Sketch a setup and measurement method that may be used to check the runout tolerance. Also show the acceptable tolerance zone.

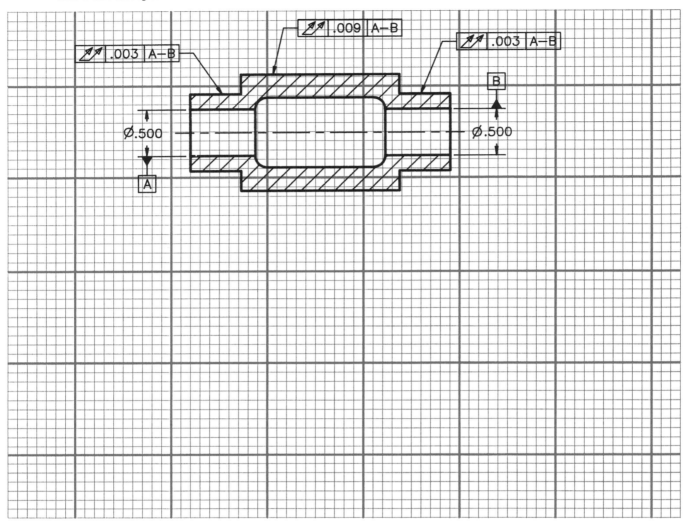

31. Sketch a setup and measurement method that may be used to check the runout tolerance. Also show the acceptable tolerance zone.

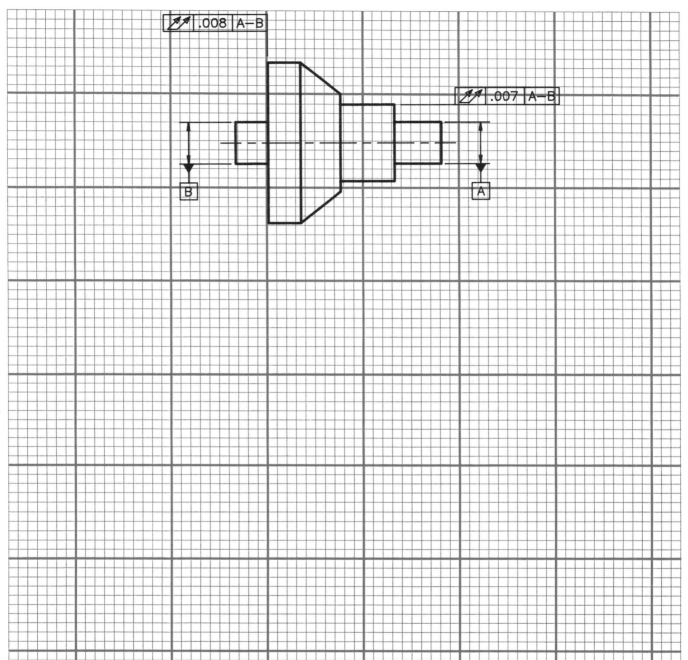

Chapter 11

PROFILE

READING

Read Chapter 11 of the *Design Dimensioning and Tolerancing* textbook prior to completing the review exercises.

OBJECTIVES

A combination of activities is required to achieve the following objectives. Completing the reading assignment and the following review exercises are an important part of achieving the objectives. Familiarization with the objectives prior to completion of the reading assignment and review exercises will make mastery of the objectives easier. After completing the reading assignment and completing the review exercises, you will be able to:
- Define line and surface profile tolerances.
- Apply profile tolerances to control a limited zone on a feature or all of a feature.
- Apply profile tolerances to extend all around the profile shown in a drawing view.
- Complete profile tolerance specifications to achieve any of the possible levels of control.
- Sketch the tolerance zone created by profile tolerance specifications.
- Specify coplanarity requirements using profile tolerances.
- Identify profile tolerances as the means for controlling conical surface form, orientation, and location.
- Draw a composite profile tolerance specification.

─────────────── REVIEW EXERCISES ───────────────

Place your answers in the spaces provided. Show all calculations for problems that require mathematical solutions.

MULTIPLE CHOICE

_____ 1. Only the _____ is different between the format of a line profile and a surface profile tolerance specification.
  A. datum referencing method
  B. use of basic dimensions
  C. all around symbol usage
  D. tolerance symbol

_____ 2. If a profile tolerance _____, it does not control the location or orientation of the toleranced surface.
  A. is a line profile control
  B. is a surface profile control
  C. does not include datum references
  D. All of the above.

_____ 3. Profile of a line is similar to _____ tolerances since individual line elements are controlled separately.
  A. straightness
  B. flatness
  C. perpendicularity
  D. angularity

_____ 4. A profile tolerance may be applied to less than a whole surface by defining and referencing _____.
 A. limits of size
 B. limits of application
 C. dual requirements
 D. datums

_____ 5. Unless indicated otherwise, profile tolerances are assumed to be _____.
 A. unilateral
 B. bilateral
 C. all around
 D. applied on the basis of MMC

_____ 6. Unilateral profile tolerances may be applied to control _____.
 A. form
 B. form and orientation
 C. form, orientation, and size
 D. Any of the above.

_____ 7. Datum references are included in a profile tolerance only if _____ is to be controlled.
 A. form
 B. form and orientation
 C. form, orientation, and size
 D. Either B or C.

_____ 8. A basic dimension is used to locate a feature controlled by a profile tolerance only if _____ is to be controlled.
 A. form
 B. form and orientation
 C. form, orientation, and size
 D. Either B or C.

_____ 9. To control form only, _____ datum reference(s) must be used.
 A. no
 B. one
 C. two
 D. three

_____ 10. If a profile tolerance includes datum references, the minimum specified amount of control is _____.
 A. form
 B. form and orientation
 C. form, orientation, and size
 D. None of the above.

_____ 11. The allowable form variations of a cone may be specified with a surface profile tolerance that references _____, and no requirement on the orientation of the cone would be included in the profile tolerance.
 A. no datums
 B. one datum
 C. a datum axis
 D. All of the above.

TRUE/FALSE

_____ 12. Profile tolerances are always specified with the MMC modifier. (A)True or (B)False?

_____ 13. A curved surface must be defined by basic dimensions when a profile tolerance is applied to the surface. (A)True or (B)False?

_____ 14. Surface profile may only be used to control the form of a curved surface. (A)True or (B)False?

_____ 15. Even when an all around symbol is used, profile tolerances do not extend past abrupt changes in direction. (A)True or (B)False?

_____ 16. A line drawn to indicate a unilateral profile tolerance is not required to extend along the full limits of application. (A)True or (B)False?

_____ 17. When used, unilateral profile tolerances must be applied to permit a plus size tolerance rather than a minus size tolerance. (A)True or (B)False?

_____ 18. A feature controlled by a profile tolerance may be located by a basic dimension if the profile tolerance includes the necessary datum references. (A)True or (B)False?

_____ 19. A composite profile tolerance may be used to specify a small tolerance for form of a surface and a large tolerance for the form, orientation, and location relative to one or more datums. (A)True or (B)False?

_____ 20. One method of specifying coplanarity of multiple flat surfaces is to apply a flatness tolerance. (A)True or (B)False?

FILL IN THE BLANK

_____ 21. There are _____ levels of control that may be specified with either of the profile tolerance types.

_____ 22. _____ profile tolerance may be applied to a surface, but it only controls individual line elements on the surface.

_____ 23. Profile tolerances apply along the entire surface to which they are applied, and the limits of the surface are defined by _____ changes in direction.

_____ 24. A _____ line is drawn to one side of a feature outline to indicate that a profile tolerance is unilateral.

_____ 25. The information shown in the _____ only partially determines the level of control established by a profile tolerance specification.

_____ 26. No _____ is required in a profile tolerance specification when controlling form only.

_____ 27. Dimensions that define the shape of a surface must be _____ if a profile tolerance is applied.

SHORT ANSWER

28. Profile tolerances are typically attached to a controlled surface in what manner? _____

_____

_____

29. How would a profile tolerance that applies all the way around a feature profile be indicated?

_____

_____

_____

30. Describe a unilateral profile tolerance and how it is applied on a drawing. _____

_____

_____

_____

_____

_____

31. Explain the impact of applying a plus or minus tolerance on the location dimension for a surface that is controlled by a profile tolerance that includes datum references. _____

_____

_____

_____

_____

32. Place an X by each characteristic that affects the required level of control on a feature.

_____ Line or surface profile symbol

_____ Datum references

_____ Total area of the controlled surface

_____ Basic or coordinate tolerance location dimensions

_____ Curved or flat surface

33. How can a coplanarity requirement for multiple flat surfaces be specified? _____

_____

_____

APPLICATION PROBLEMS

All application problems are to be completed using correct dimensioning techniques. Show any required calculations.

34. Apply a line profile tolerance that only controls the form of the curved surface within a boundary .025″ wide.

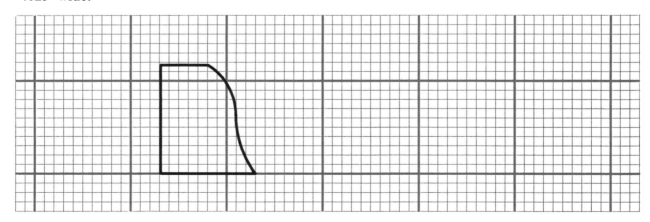

35. Show the tolerance zone created by each of the given tolerance specifications. Superimpose the tolerance zone on the given drawing.

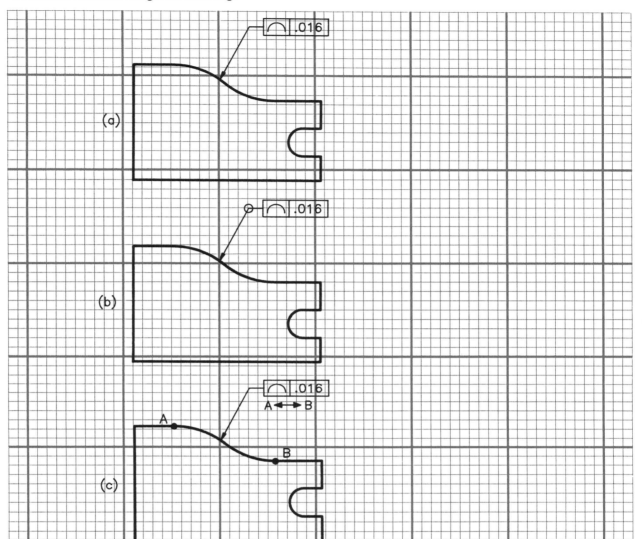

36. Complete the drawing to the extent necessary to control the line profile all around the perimeter of the part within a boundary .040″ wide. Indicate basic dimensions where they are needed.

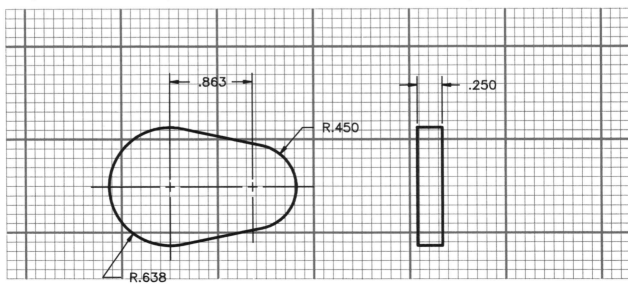

37. Control the line profile of the given slot all around within a unilateral zone .015″ to the outside (larger). Also, control both location and orientation of the slot to three datums using the same tolerance specification. Indicate basic dimensions where they are needed.

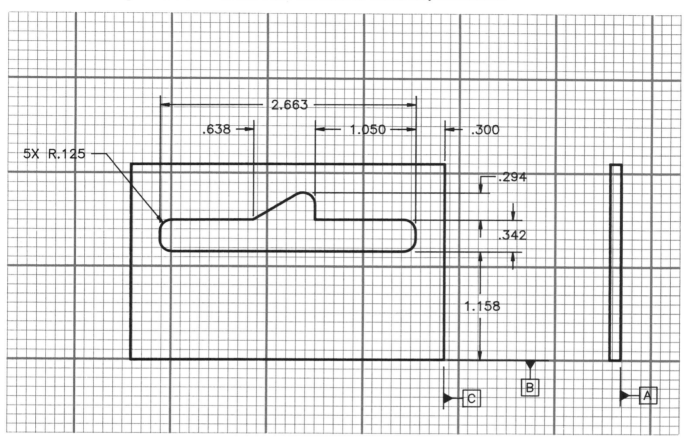

38. Show the tolerance zone for the given slot. Superimpose the tolerance zone on the given drawing.

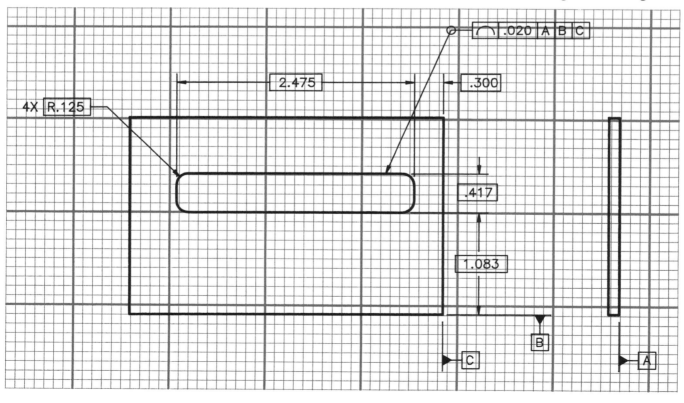

39. Control the form and size of the punched hole within a surface profile of .010″. Permit location error of ± .010″ in the X and Y coordinate.

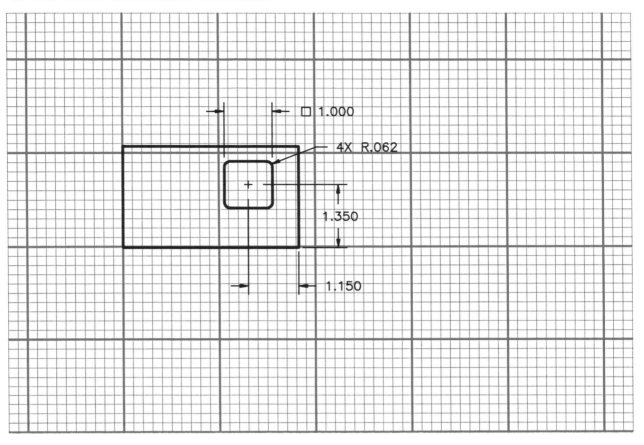

40. Require flat and coplanar bosses within a .008″ tolerance zone. Allow location and parallelism within ± .015″ relative to the bottom surface.

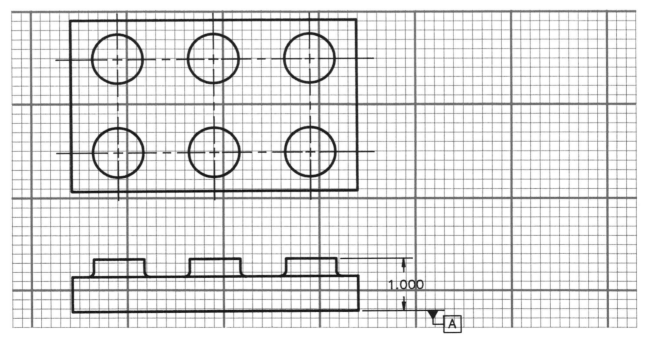

41. Require flat and coplanar bosses within a .008″ tolerance zone. Require the zone to be centered 1.000″ from datum A and parallel to datum A.

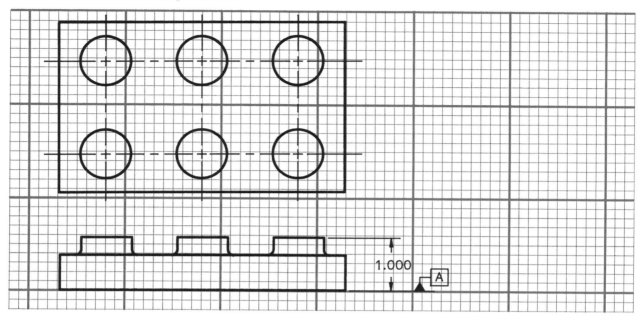

42. Specify a tolerance zone that controls the cone surface size and form within a boundary that is .018″ wide and centered on datum axis A.

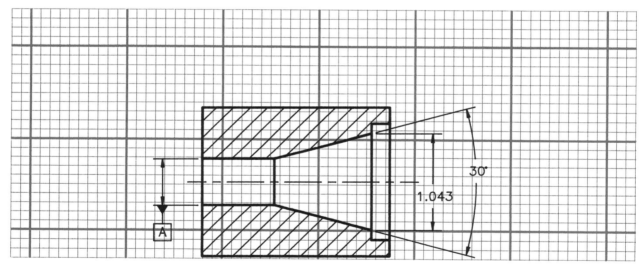

43. Apply a composite profile tolerance to establish a zone .005″ wide so that the coplanar surfaces must be located and parallel to datum A within .025″.

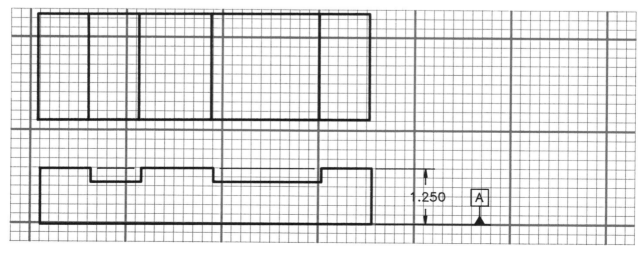

Chapter 12

PRACTICAL APPLICATIONS AND CALCULATION METHODS

READING

Read Chapter 12 of the *Design Dimensioning and Tolerancing* textbook prior to completing the review exercises.

OBJECTIVES

A combination of activities is required to achieve the following objectives. Completing the reading assignment and the following review exercises are an important part of achieving the objectives. Familiarization with the objectives prior to completion of the reading assignment and review exercises will make mastery of the objectives easier. After completing the reading assignment and completing the review exercises, you will be able to:

- Calculate position tolerances when more than two parts are stacked in a floating fastener or fixed fastener application.
- Distribute the total available position tolerance between features to which position tolerances are applied.
- Specify projected tolerance zones for fixed feature locations to prevent interference conditions.
- Determine the amount of tolerance accumulation in a simple assembly.
- Properly use zero position tolerances at MMC to increase manufacturing freedom.
- Apply paper gaging techniques to determine if a produced part meets drawing requirements.

───────────────── **REVIEW EXERCISES** ─────────────────

Place your answers in the spaces provided. Show all calculations for problems that require mathematical solutions.

MULTIPLE CHOICE

_____ 1. If edges of stacked parts in a floating fastener condition must align, then the edges are referenced as _____ in the tolerance specification.
   A. origins
   B. datum features
   C. primary surfaces
   D. mated surfaces

_____ 2. When using the formula T = H - F to calculate one position tolerance value for both parts in a floating fastener condition, the holes _____.
   A. must be the same specified size
   B. may be different specified sizes
   C. must be smaller than the value used for H
   D. None of the above.

_____ 3. To increase the allowable amount of tolerance, what can be specified when alignment of datum features is not required?
   A. Specify a composite position tolerance.
   B. Specify a bonus tolerance.
   C. Specify a large pattern locating tolerance.
   D. Both A and C.

4. In a floating fastener application, the correct amount of position tolerance for a .190″ diameter bolt and .228″ MMC diameter hole is _____ inch.
   A. .014
   B. .019
   C. .028
   D. .038

5. Two of three stacked parts must have _____ in a fixed fastener condition.
   A. threads
   B. press fit sizes
   C. clearance holes
   D. None of the above.

6. The allowable position tolerance that can be applied to each part in a fixed fastener application is _____ inch if the clearance hole is .282″ diameter MMC and a .250″ diameter bolt is used.
   A. .014
   B. .016
   C. .028
   D. .032

7. Generally, a threaded hole is given _____ the clearance hole to improve producibility.
   A. more position tolerance than
   B. the same position tolerance as
   C. less position tolerance than
   D. None of the above.

8. A projected tolerance zone is indicated by a(n) _____.
   A. letter P inside a circle
   B. arrow pointing to the outside of the part
   C. note under the feature control frame
   D. All of the above.

9. A projected tolerance zone is typically specified to extend a distance equal to the _____.
   A. fastener length
   B. length of the fixed segment of the fixed fastener
   C. clearance feature length
   D. fastener diameter

10. A hole size specification of .210″ minimum and .216″ maximum diameter has a position tolerance specification of .020″ diameter MMC. A .190″ diameter floating fastener passes through the hole. If the hole is produced at .208″ diameter and has a position error of .012″ diameter, what should be done?
    A. Accept the part since it meets the specification.
    B. Accept the part since it is functional.
    C. Reject the part and throw it away.
    D. Rework the part to make the hole an acceptable diameter.

11. A hole size specification of .385″ minimum and .395″ maximum diameter has a position tolerance specification of .010″ diameter MMC. If the position tolerance is changed to .000″ diameter MMC, a minimum hole diameter of _____ inch must be specified with the maximum size limit remaining .395″.
    A. .375
    B. .380
    C. .385
    D. .390

_____ 12. Concentric circles used to paper gage a feature relating tolerance requirement _____ relative to the graph origin.
A. must be centered
B. are free to float
C. are offset a distance equal to the location of the nearest hole
D. None of the above.

_____ 13. If a single line tolerance specification does not include any datum references, the tolerance is either _____.
A. form or runout
B. form or orientation
C. form or profile
D. profile or orientation

_____ 14. A single feature may require a maximum of _____ level(s) of control, each specified in a separate feature control frame line.
A. no
B. one
C. two
D. None of the above.

_____ 15. A flat surface may have a perpendicularity tolerance of .017″ applied to it and also have a _____ tolerance of .008″ applied to further refine the surface form.
A. flatness
B. parallelism
C. position
D. circularity

TRUE/FALSE

_____ 16. A floating fastener condition exists only when a maximum of two stacked parts have clearance holes through which a fastener passes. (A)True or (B)False?

_____ 17. If the clearance holes in mating parts are the same size, different position tolerance values may be applied on each hole. (A)True or (B)False?

_____ 18. If one part is purchased with hole position tolerances already specified by the manufacturer, it is not possible to calculate position tolerances for the mating parts. (A)True or (B)False?

_____ 19. A projected tolerance zone extends the full length of the controlled feature plus a projected distance outside the feature. (A)True or (B)False?

_____ 20. A specified zero position tolerance at MMC is an error since perfect position is seldom, if ever, achieved. (A)True or (B)False?

_____ 21. Even if a part is functionally adequate, the part must be rejected, reworked, or accepted by special procedures if it does not meet drawing requirements. (A)True or (B)False?

_____ 22. Paper gaging should only be used for position tolerances specified with the MMC modifier. (A)True or (B)False?

_____ 23. Zero position tolerances should not be specified with the RFS modifier. (A)True or (B)False?

_____ 24. Paper gaging of the feature relating tolerance in a composite position tolerance specification can be completed by plotting the hole-to-hole measurements without concern for the hole locations relative to any datums. (A)True or (B)False?

FILL IN THE BLANK

_____ 25. Show the formula used to calculate floating fastener condition dimensions for two parts that must have aligned surfaces.

_____ 26. Complete the formula used to calculate unevenly distributed tolerances when both holes are the same specified size. $T_1 + T_2 =$ _____ $- 2F$

_____ 27. What is the formula for calculating distributed tolerances in a floating fastener application in which two hole sizes are specified?

_____ 28. When more than two parts are stacked in a fixed fastener condition, tolerances are calculated considering _____ parts at a time if the clearance holes are different diameters.

_____ 29. Evenly distributed position tolerances for a fixed fastener condition are calculated using what formula?

_____ 30. The total available position tolerance for a fixed fastener condition may be distributed between two parts using what formula?

_____ 31. A _____ tolerance zone controls the location outside of the toleranced feature.

_____ 32. A correctly specified _____ position tolerance at MMC results in all functionally good parts being acceptable.

_____ 33. A specified hole diameter of .163″ minimum and .168″ maximum has a specified position tolerance of .025″ diameter at LMC. A produced hole of .165″ diameter has an allowable position tolerance of _____ inch diameter.

SHORT ANSWER

34. If three stacked parts all have the same diameter clearance holes, how are position tolerances for the holes calculated? _____

_____

35. If the total allowable position tolerance for a fixed fastener application is .022″, what would be wrong with applying .020″ diameter tolerance on one part and .002″ diameter tolerance on the other part?

_____

_____

_____

36. Describe a fixed fastener condition. _____

_____

_____

_____

37. Why is the manufacturing process considered when distributing tolerances between two parts in a fixed fastener condition? _____

_____

_____

_____

38. Why is it sometimes necessary to show the direction that a projected tolerance zone extends?

_____

_____

_____

_____

39. A hole for a .250″ diameter bolt is specified to have a .260″ minimum and .268″ maximum diameter with a position tolerance of .010″ diameter at MMC. What can be done to the hole size and tolerance specifications to maximize manufacturing freedom? _____

_____

_____

_____

APPLICATION PROBLEMS

All application problems are to be completed using correct dimensioning techniques. Show any required calculations.

40. Complete a composite position tolerance that may be applied to the pattern of holes in each part. Bolts measuring .250″ diameter pass through the holes. The datum features on the part may be misaligned by .030″.

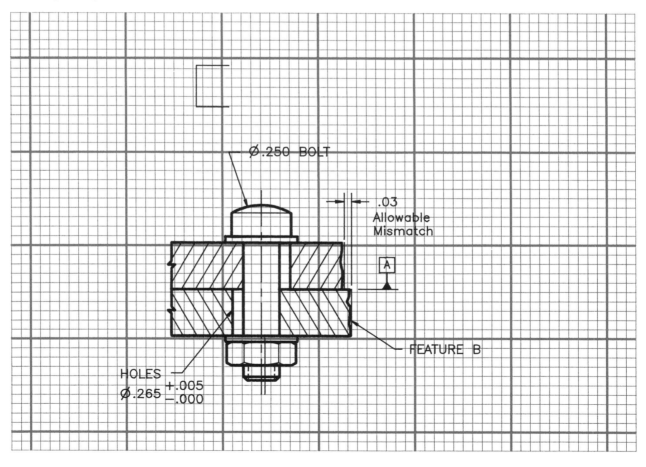

41. Apply the maximum allowable position tolerance specification on the untoleranced hole. A .375″ diameter bolt passes through the holes.

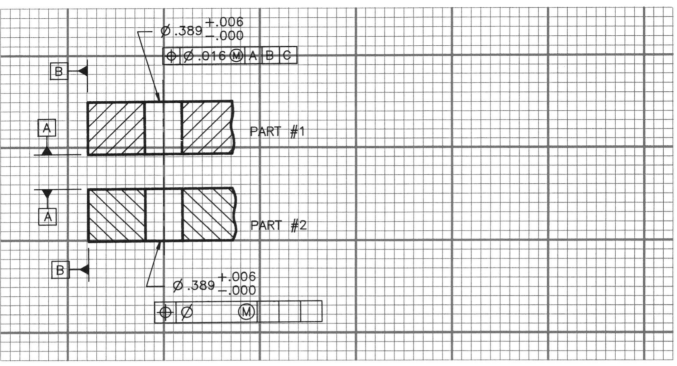

42. On the following page, draw one view of each part that shows the hole patterns. Dimension the hole pattern and apply tolerances for a fixed fastener condition with a .250″ diameter bolt and clearance holes .292″ diameter at MMC.

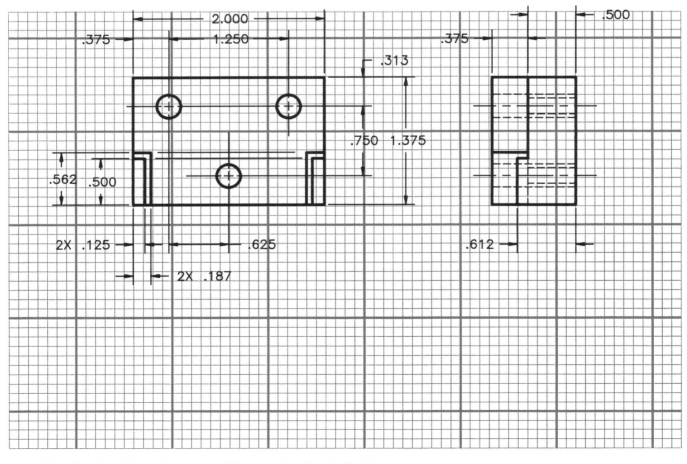

43. Calculate and apply position tolerances for the two given parts. Apply 66% of the total tolerance on the threaded holes.

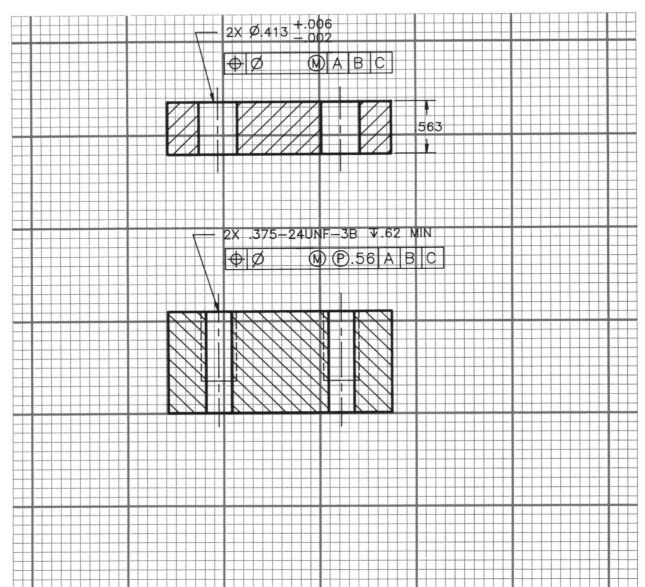

2X Ø.413 $^{+.006}_{-.002}$

⊕ | Ø | | Ⓜ | A | B | C

.563

2X .375—24UNF—3B ▽.62 MIN

⊕ | Ø | | Ⓜ | Ⓟ.56 | A | B | C

44. Show the tolerance zone for the given holes.

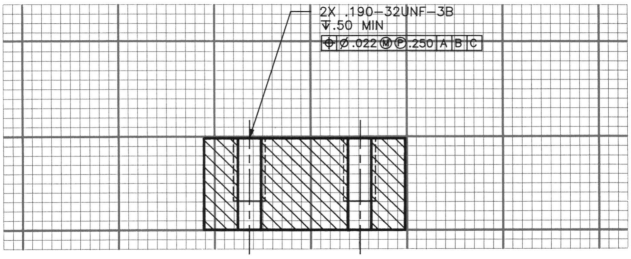

2X .190—32UNF—3B
▽.50 MIN

⊕ | Ø.022 Ⓜ Ⓟ.250 | A | B | C

45. What is the correct projected distance for a position tolerance applied to the threaded hole? Why is that distance the correct one?

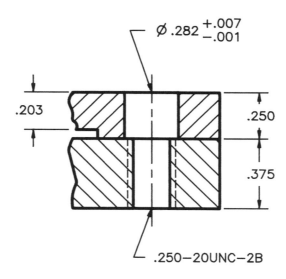

⌀ .282 +.007 −.001

.203

.250

.375

.250−20UNC−2B

_____

_____

_____

46. Apply a size tolerance of ± .030″ for the given dimension. Require the top surface to be parallel to datum A within .020″ and flat within .009″.

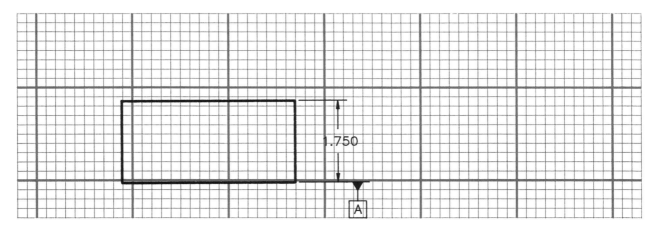

1.750

A

47. Calculate the allowable specified position tolerance for the specified clearance hole on the shown plate. Assume datums are selected to minimize tolerance stackup.

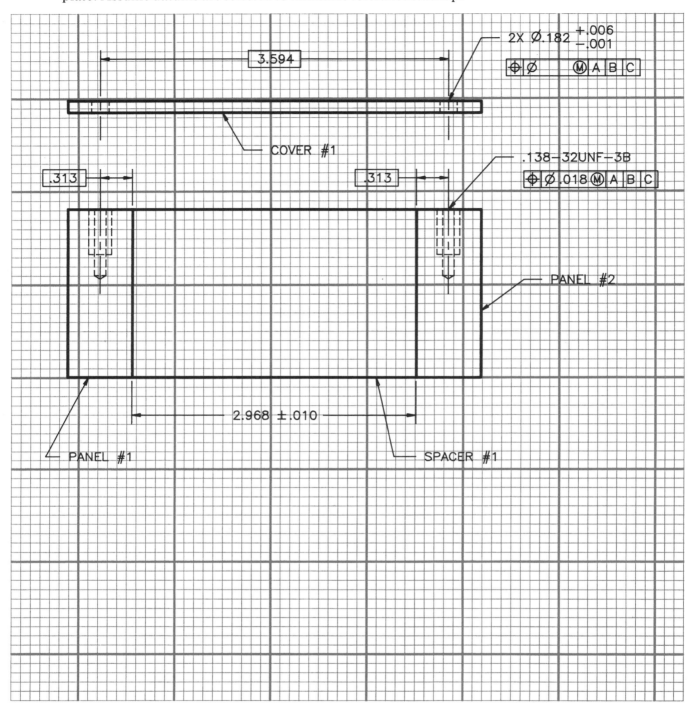